Contents

KU-685-358

T24329

The GCSE Mathematics examination will be assessed using two two tiers from 2007 for the Modular course and from 2008 for the Linear course. Students will have a choice of two tiers (Higher and Foundation) and a choice of two specifications – one Modular and one Linear. For example you may be doing a higher level GCSE which is tested at the end of the two years, i.e. the Linear course.

GCSE Mathematics coursework

Assessment objective 1 (AO1)

AO1 is known as Using and Applying Mathematics and is used to assess the coursework element of GCSE Mathematics. It is also assessed in all of the examination papers. Depending on the examination board that your school is using, coursework is assessed using one of several methods. These are as follows:

- At least one task which demonstrates ability to use and apply mathematics. These tasks can be practical or investigational and are marked by the school. They count for 10% of the final mark.

or

- At least one task which demonstrates ability to use and apply mathematics. These tasks can be practical or investigational and are marked by the exam board. They count for 10% of the final mark.

Assessment objective 4 (AO4)

AO4 is known as Handling Data. You are required to produce a project, using knowledge skills and understanding in Handling Data. This project forms part of your coursework assessment and accounts for 10% of the final mark.

For students starting their GCSE course in, or after, September 2007, there will be no coursework element. As a result the weightings of the remaining assessment components will change.

edexcel
advancing learning, changing lives

Student Book and CD-ROM

Course Companion
GCSE Mathematics

Higher Tier
Linear and Modular

Lisa Greenstein

Peter Sherran

Dr Sue Waring

A PEARSON COMPANY

Edexcel
190 High Holborn
London WC1V 7BH
UK

ISBN-10 1-84690-162-6 **ISBN-13** 978-1-84690-162-6

Printed and bound in Great Britain by Scotprint
Prepared for Edexcel by Starfish Design, Editorial and Project Management Ltd
Project management by Heather Morris
Illustrated by Peters and Zabransky Ltd

The publisher's policy is to use paper manufactured from sustainable forests.

Linear GCSE

A Linear GCSE is a course where all the content of the specification is covered over a two-year period and then assessed with examinations in June of the second year.

There will be two parallel examination papers, on different days, each counting for 40% of the final mark.

Foundation Tier	Paper 1	Non-calculator	1 hour 30 minutes
Foundation Tier	Paper 2	With calculator	1 hour 30 minutes
Higher Tier	Paper 3	Non-calculator	1 hour 45 minutes
Higher Tier	Paper 4	With calculator	1 hour 45 minutes

Modular GCSE

A Modular GCSE course is where the content of the specification is broken down into units. Units 2 and 3 are assessed in November, March or June. Examinations for Unit 4 are available in June and November. The weighting of the units are as follows:

Unit 1 – Coursework which accounts for 20% of the final mark, assessed in June and November only.

Units	Unit 2 Two equal sections	Unit 3 Two equal sections	Unit 4 Two parallel terminal examination papers	
	Section A with calculator Section B non-calculator	Section A with calculator Section B non-calculator	Non-calculator paper	With calculator paper
Weighting	10% weighting	20% weighting	25% weighting	25% weighting
Foundation Tier	Paper 8 40 minutes	Paper 10 1 hour	Paper 12 1 hour	Paper 13 1 hour
Higher Tier	Paper 9 40 minutes	Paper 11 1 hour	Paper 14 1 hour 10 minutes	Paper 15 1 hour 10 minutes

General advice on how to achieve a Grade A

These statements give a general indication of the standards you will need to achieve to obtain a Grade A. Your final grade will depend on how well you have met the assessment objectives overall. Shortcomings in some areas may be balanced by better performance in others.

- A Grade A candidate must be able to give reasons for the choices they make when investigating within mathematics itself or when using mathematics to analyse tasks; these reasons explain why particular lines of enquiry or procedures are followed and others rejected. Candidates apply the mathematics they know in familiar and unfamiliar contexts. Candidates use mathematical language and symbols effectively in presenting a convincing and reasoned argument. Their reports include mathematical justifications, explaining their solutions to problems involving a number of features or variables.

- Candidates manipulate simple surds. They determine the bounds of intervals. Candidates understand and use direct and inverse proportion. They manipulate algebraic formulae, equations and expressions, finding common factors and multiplying two linear expressions. In simplifying algebraic expressions, they use rules of indices for negative and fractional values. They solve problems using intersections and gradients of graphs.

- Candidates sketch the graphs of sine, cosine and tangent functions for any angle and generate and interpret graphs based on these functions. Candidates use sine, cosine and tangent of angles of any size, and Pythagoras' theorem, when solving problems in two and three dimensions. They use the conditions for congruent triangles in formal geometric proofs. They calculate lengths of circular arcs and areas of sectors, and calculate the surface area of cylinders and volumes of cones and spheres. They understand and use the effect of enlargement on areas and volumes of shapes and solids.

- Candidates interpret and construct histograms. They understand how different methods of sampling and different sample sizes may affect the reliability of conclusions drawn; they select and justify a sample and method to investigate a population. They recognise when and how to work with probabilities associated with independent and mutually exclusive events.

Key facts

- A factor of x is a number which divides into x an exact number of times. For example, the factors of 12 are 1, 2, 3, 4, 6 and 12

- A multiple of x is a number which divides exactly by x. For example, 9 is a multiple of 3

- To square a number, multiply the number by itself. For example, $4^2 = 4 \times 4 = 16$ The positive **square root** of 16 is 4 or $\sqrt{16} = 4$

- The cube of a number n is the product of $n \times n \times n$. For example, $4^3 = 64$ The cube root of 64 is 4 or $\sqrt[3]{64} = 4$

- A power (or index) tells us how many times to multiply a number by itself. For example, 2^5 (2 to the power of 5) $= 2 \times 2 \times 2 \times 2 \times 2$

- To find the reciprocal of a number, divide 1 by the number. The reciprocal of 2 or $\frac{2}{1}$ is $\frac{1}{2}$ The reciprocal of $\frac{3}{4}$ is $\frac{4}{3}$ or $1\frac{1}{3}$

- You can express any integer as the product of **prime numbers**. A prime factor is a factor that is also a prime number. For example, $30 = 2 \times 15 = 2 \times 3 \times 5$

- The highest common factor (HCF) is the largest integer that divides exactly into each of a given set of numbers. For example, the HCF of 8 and 20 is 4

- The lowest common multiple (LCM) is the smallest number into which all of a given set of numbers will divide exactly. For example, the LCM of 4, 5 and 6 is 60

- When you multiply or divide two **directed numbers**, remember this rule. If the signs are the same, the answer is positive. If the signs are different the answer is negative. For example,

$p \times q = pq$

$-p \times q = -pq$

$-p \times -q = pq$

❶ Examiner's tips

- When you solve problems using several operations, always follow the BIDMAS rule for the order of operations (Brackets, Indices, Division, Multiplication, Addition, Subtraction).
- Practise solving arithmetical expressions using a scientific calculator. Make sure you know where to find the keys that find: squares (x^2), cubes (x^3), powers (y^x) or (Λ).
- A negative index tells you to use a reciprocal, so

$$2^{-1} = \frac{1}{2}$$

$$2^{-3} = \frac{1}{2^3} = \frac{1}{2 \times 2 \times 2} = \frac{1}{8}$$

This is why the reciprocal button on a calculator usually looks like ($\frac{1}{x}$) or (x^{-1}).

Can you answer these questions?

1. From the set {8, 9, 10, 11, 12, 13, 14, 15, 16} write down:
   - (a) all the even numbers
   - (b) all the odd numbers
   - (c) all the prime numbers
   - (d) all the square numbers
   - (e) all the multiples of 3
   - (f) all the factors of 60

2. Write the following numbers as products of their prime factors.
   - (a) 490
   - (b) 250
   - (c) 28

3. Work out
   - (a) 23^2
   - (b) 118^2
   - (c) $\sqrt{144}$
   - (d) $\sqrt{9216}$
   - (e) $2^4 \times 3^4$
   - (f) $(1.8)^3$
   - (g) $7^3 \div 2^4$
   - (h) $\dfrac{(6.7 - 5.2)^2}{0.25}$

4. Calculate without using a calculator.
   - (a) $-19 + (-128)$
   - (b) $-15 + 242$
   - (c) $345 - 810$
   - (d) $-150 - (-150)$
   - (e) $245 + 128 \times -2$
   - (f) $-(15 + 399) \div -3$
   - (g) $-416 \div \frac{1}{4} + (6 \text{ squared})$

5. Find the reciprocals of these numbers.
   - (a) 10
   - (b) $\frac{1}{25}$
   - (c) $5\frac{6}{7}$
   - (d) 1.15
   - (e) $\sqrt{144}$

Key facts

- Angles may be acute (< 90°), obtuse (between 90° and 180°) or reflex (between 180° and 360°).

- When naming angles the letter at the vertex is in the middle.

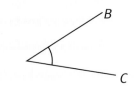

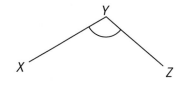

angle *BAC* is acute   angle *XYZ* is obtuse   reflex angles

- The first fact about angles is: a complete turn is 360°.

- These facts now follow:

a right angle is 90° as it is a quarter turn

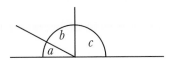

angles on a straight line add to 180°

$a + b + c = 180°$ (half a complete turn)

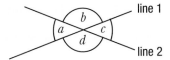

opposite angles are equal

$a + b = 180°$ (on line 1)

$b + c = 180°$ (on line 2)

so $a = c$ and $b = d$

- The second fact is that corresponding angles are equal, because the parallel lines which form them run in the same direction.

$a = b$

Look for 'F'. Wherever you find corresponding angles, the lines form an 'F' shape.

- These facts may now be deduced.

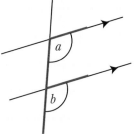

alternate angles (between parallels) are equal

$a + b = 180°$ (angles on straight line)

$c + d = 180°$ (angles on straight line)

but $b = d$ (corresponding angles)

So $a = c$

Look for the 'Z' shape for alternate angles.

▶ *continued*

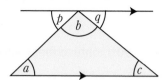

angles in a triangle add up to 180°

$a = p$ (alternate angles)

$c = q$ (alternate angles)

$p + b + q = 180°$ (angles on straight line)

So $a + b + c = 180°$

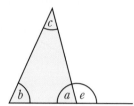

exterior angle of a triangle equals the sum of the interior opposite angles

$a + b + c = 180°$ (angles in a triangle)

$a + e = 180°$ (angles on straight line)

So $e = b + c$

- **Triangles** may be named by their largest angle or by their sides.

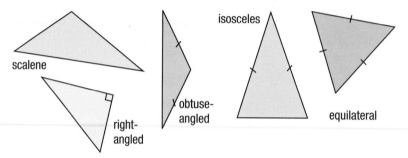

scalene

right-angled

obtuse-angled

isosceles

equilateral

- The base angles of an isosceles triangle are equal

- All angles in an equilateral triangle are equal to 60°.

- Diagonals are straight lines joining 2 vertices of a polygon.

- Triangles and quadrilaterals are examples of polygons, which are closed plane shapes with straight sides.

Names and angles in regular polygons – n represents the number of sides

n	Name	Angle sum	Interior angle	Exterior angle
3	Triangle	180°	60°	120°
4	Quadrilateral	360°	90°	90°
5	Pentagon	540°	108°	72°
6	Hexagon	720°	120°	60°
7	Heptagon	900°	128.6°	51.4°
8	Octagon	1080°	135°	45°

- A polygon with n sides may be cut into $(n - 2)$ triangles and so the sum of all the interior angles is $(n - 2) \times 180°$

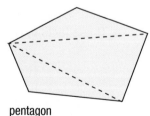

pentagon

5 sides

5 – 2 = 3 triangles

angle sum = $3 \times 180°$

= 540°

- For a regular polygon with n sides: exterior angle = $\dfrac{360}{n}$

interior angle = 180° – exterior angle

▶ *continued*

- When angles are used practically, such as in surveying or navigating, some are named, e.g. angles of elevation and depression.

- Bearings are measured clockwise from north and are always quoted using 3 figures.

❶ Examiner's tips

- Diagrams given in questions are very useful – read them carefully.
- Mark all given information, and your deductions, on a diagram.
- Turning diagrams round and adding coloured lines may help.

Worked example

Find the sizes of the angles marked with letters. Give reasons.

Solution

Notice only one pair of lines is parallel.

$a = 73°$ (alternate angles are equal)

$b = 107°$ (angles on a straight line sum to 180°)

$c = 85°$ (opposite angles are equal)

$a + b + c = 73° + 107° + 85° = 265°$

$d = 95°$ (angle sum of quadrilateral is 360°
and $360° - 265° = 95°$)

Can you answer these questions?

1. Find the sizes of the angles marked with letters. Give reasons.

(a)

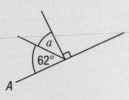

AB is a straight line

(b)

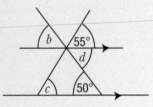

2. Find (a) x

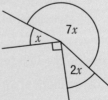

(b) y

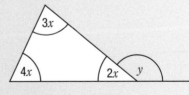

3. State the sizes of all the angles in a right-angled isosceles triangle.

4. The angles of a quadrilateral are x, $2x$, $3x$, and $4x$. Find x.

5. Calculate the size of an exterior and an interior angle in a regular 9-sided polygon (nonagon).

Key facts

- The pattern of crosses on a **scatter graph** may be used to decide what kind of relationship, if any, exists between the quantities shown.

- If there is a relationship, or **correlation**, between the quantities then a line of best fit may be drawn that passes near all of the plotted points.

- If there is no pattern, so that no line of best fit may be drawn, then there is no correlation, or zero correlation, between the quantities

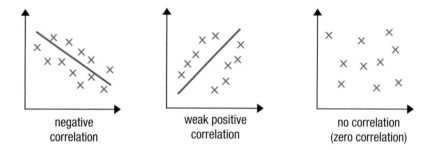

positive correlation   negative correlation   weak positive correlation   no correlation (zero correlation)

- The closer the points are to the line of best fit, the stronger the correlation.

- If the points are not close to the line, the correlation is weak, or low.

- The line of best fit may be used to estimate the value of one quantity corresponding to a known value of the other. For example, this scatter graph shows a strong positive correlation between the marks of pupils in two separate maths tests.

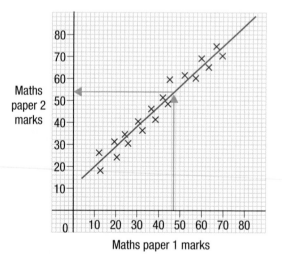

A pupil who scored 47 marks on the first test, missed the second test. Using the line of best fit, an estimated mark of 54 is obtained for this pupil.

- The method of using the line of best fit to estimate an unknown value may be unreliable, or even meaningless, if used outside the range of plotted points.

❶ Examiner's tips

- When asked to describe the correlation between two quantities, state whether it is positive, negative or zero.

Can you answer these questions?

1. Describe the correlation that you would expect to find between these quantities.

    (a) the size of an engine and its power output

    (b) the size of a star and its distance from Earth

    (c) the outside temperature and the number of woolly jumpers sold.

2. (a) The table shows the number of 'finishers' of the London Marathon over the first twenty years that the event has taken place, apart from the figure for 1995 which is missing. Show this information on a scatter graph and draw a line of best fit to estimate the number of finishers in 1995.

Number of finishers of the London Marathon 1981–2000

Year	Number of finishers	Year	Number of finishers
1981	6418	1991	23 080
1982	15 758	1992	23 657
1983	15 776	1993	24 369
1984	15 649	1994	25 000
1985	15 841	1995	
1986	18 031	1996	26 000
1987	19 970	1997	29 000
1988	21 100	1998	30 000
1989	22 651	1999	30 700
1990	24 871	2000	32 600

(b) Comment on the proposal to predict the number of finishers in 2020 by extending the line of best fit.

4 Fractions

Have you ever wondered?

A unit fraction has 1 as its numerator. The greater the denominator of a fraction, the smaller the value of the fraction. Why is this?

You know that to simplify a fraction, you divide the numerator and denominator by the same number. Do you know how this works? (Hint: Think about fractions that are equivalent to 1.)

Key facts

- A fraction is a number that represents an integer divided by another integer, e.g. $3 \div 4 = \frac{3}{4}$

- The upper integer in the fraction is called the numerator and the lower integer in the fraction is called the denominator.

- You can represent a fraction as a shape divided into a number of equal parts with a number of parts shaded. The number of parts in the whole shape gives you the denominator. The number of shaded parts gives you the numerator.

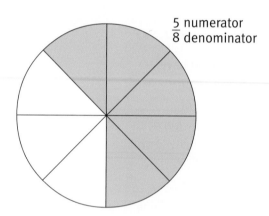

$\frac{5 \text{ numerator}}{8 \text{ denominator}}$

Did you know?

- The ancient Romans did not use fractions. The concept of fractions was developed by Hindu mathematicians from about AD 500. The Romans also did not have a concept of zero!

❶ Examiner's tips

- For addition and subtraction problems, use **equivalent fractions** to help you find the lowest common denominator (LCD). For example,

$\frac{1}{2} + \frac{2}{5}$ The LCM of 2 and 5 is 10. So the LCD is 10

$\frac{1}{2} + \frac{2}{5} = \frac{5}{10} + \frac{4}{10} = \frac{9}{10}$

- For multiplication and division problems, the fractions do not need to have the same denominators, but you will need to convert **mixed numbers** to **improper fractions**. For example,

$\frac{1}{3} \times 5\frac{1}{6} = \frac{1}{3} \times \frac{31}{6} = \frac{31}{18} = 1\frac{13}{18}$ Give your answer as a mixed number.

- To divide by a fraction, invert the fraction. Then multiply by the inverted fraction. For example,

$1\frac{2}{3} \div \frac{4}{5} = \frac{5}{3} \div \frac{4}{5} = \frac{5}{3} \times \frac{5}{4} = \frac{25}{12} = 2\frac{1}{12}$ Give your answer as a mixed number.

- For all problems, give answers in the lowest (simplest) terms and as mixed numbers if necessary.

Definitions

- **Proper fraction**
  a fraction with denominator greater than its numerator and so with value less than 1
- **Improper fraction**
  a fraction with numerator greater than its denominator and so with value more than 1
- **Mixed number**
  consists of whole number and proper fraction
- **Equivalent fractions**
  have equal values but different numerators and denominators, e.g. $\frac{1}{2} = \frac{3}{6}$

Can you answer these questions?

1. Complete the equivalent fractions.

   (a) $\frac{1}{2} = \frac{?}{4}$ (b) $\frac{3}{5} = \frac{?}{10}$ (c) $\frac{3}{8} = \frac{?}{40}$ (d) $\frac{4}{6} = \frac{?}{3}$ (e) $\frac{25}{50} = \frac{?}{2}$

   (f) $\frac{?}{4} = \frac{12}{16}$ (g) $\frac{15}{81} = \frac{5}{?}$ (h) $\frac{11}{33} = \frac{?}{3}$ (i) $\frac{95}{5} = \frac{?}{1}$

2. Write these fractions in their simplest terms.

   (a) $\frac{80}{100}$ (b) $\frac{56}{72}$ (c) $\frac{12}{60}$ (d) $\frac{65}{70}$

3. Convert these mixed numbers to improper fractions.

   (a) $9\frac{7}{8}$ (b) $45\frac{1}{3}$ (c) $12\frac{1}{2}$ (d) $14\frac{4}{5}$

4. Convert these improper fractions to mixed numbers.

   (a) $\frac{95}{12}$ (b) $\frac{47}{3}$ (c) $\frac{18}{11}$ (d) $\frac{155}{12}$

5. Calculate these. Give your answers in their simplest terms, and as mixed numbers if necessary.

   (a) $\frac{3}{4} + \frac{4}{7}$ (b) $\frac{9}{10} - \frac{1}{2}$ (c) $\frac{7}{16} + \frac{1}{3}$

   (d) $4\frac{1}{2} - 3\frac{1}{3}$ (e) $6\frac{1}{5} + 4\frac{3}{4}$ (f) $11\frac{19}{25} - 8\frac{1}{100}$

   (g) $2\frac{3}{4} - 1\frac{1}{2} - \frac{1}{4}$ (h) $7\frac{1}{2} + 3\frac{3}{8} - 1\frac{2}{3}$ (i) $5\frac{7}{12} - 1\frac{3}{5} + 2\frac{1}{6}$

6. Solve these multiplication problems.

   (a) $\frac{1}{2} \times \frac{4}{9}$ (b) $\frac{3}{4} \times \frac{1}{4}$ (c) $\frac{23}{24} \times \frac{4}{5}$

   (d) $\frac{5}{7} \times 2\frac{1}{2}$ (e) $\frac{1}{2} \times 1\frac{1}{6} \times \frac{4}{5}$ (f) $7\frac{5}{6} \times 1\frac{1}{2} \times \frac{3}{4}$

7. Solve these division problems.

   (a) $\frac{1}{4} \div \frac{1}{5}$ (b) $\frac{4}{5} \div \frac{1}{20}$ (c) $\frac{19}{15} \div \frac{2}{3}$

   (d) $6\frac{1}{3} \div \frac{1}{6}$ (e) $8\frac{3}{4} \div 1\frac{1}{2}$ (f) $12\frac{99}{100} \div 2\frac{1}{5}$

8. Solve these mixed problems.

   (a) $\frac{1}{3} + \frac{8}{9} \div \frac{1}{3}$ (b) $\frac{1}{4} \times \frac{9}{10} + \frac{1}{3}$ (c) $\frac{6}{7} \times 1\frac{3}{5} + 54\frac{7}{12} \div 1\frac{3}{4}$

   (d) $\frac{1}{2} \times \frac{1}{100} + \frac{1}{2} \times \frac{1}{100}$ (e) $7\frac{5}{8} \div (\frac{1}{3} + \frac{1}{4} + \frac{1}{2})$ (f) $3\frac{1}{3} \times 4\frac{1}{4} \times 5\frac{1}{5}$

   (g) $17\frac{3}{4} + \frac{3}{4}$ of 50   (h) $\frac{2}{3}$ of $144 \div 1\frac{1}{2}$

9. Solve these word problems.

   (a) A fabric seller wants to cut the leftover piece from a roll of cloth into scraps to sell. Each scrap piece must be $\frac{1}{4}$ metre long. She has the following left-over pieces to use: $2\frac{1}{2}$ metres of red fabric, 5 metres of green fabric and $6\frac{3}{4}$ metres of blue fabric. How many scraps can she make altogether?

   (b) A fruit vendor sells watermelons either whole, in halves, in quarters or in thirds. On a day in summer, she sells 5 halves, 7 quarters and 5 thirds as well as 4 whole melons. How many has she sold altogether? Use multiplication to help you find your answer.

Look on the CD for more exam practice questions

5 Expressions and sequences

Key facts

- Algebra is a language for expressing mathematical connections precisely. It uses letters to represent variables, usually numbers, and the same operations as calculations with numbers.

- A variable has an unknown or unfixed value and a constant is known or fixed.

- A coefficient is a numerical multiplier.

- **Rules for algebra**
  A sign applies to the term after it.
  Multiplication signs are usually omitted.
  Repeated multiplication uses index notation.
  Division is replaced with a fraction.
  Coefficients are usually written before a variable.
  Only like terms may be added and subtracted.

- An expression includes variables with constants and signs.

- The index laws are used when simplifying expressions with repeated multiplication and/or division.

Law	Rule	Example
1 $x^m \times x^n = x^{m+n}$	add the indices	$x^3 \times x^4 = x^{3+4} = x^7$
2 $x^m \div x^n = x^{m-n}$	subtract the indices	$x^6 \div x^4 = x^{6-4} = x^2$
3 $(x^m)^n = x^{mn}$	multiply the indices	$(x^3)^2 = x^{3\times2} = x^6$

Special cases of **2**: if $m = n$: $1 = x^0$ $\qquad$ $5^3 \div 5^3 = 1$ and $5^3 \div 5^3 = 5^0$

$\qquad\qquad\qquad$ if $m = 0$: $\dfrac{1}{x^n} = x^{-n}$, $\qquad$ $2^0 \div 2^3 = 2^{-3}$ and $1 \div 2^3 = \dfrac{1}{2^3}$

- A general term of a sequence is a rule for working out particular terms. The rule may be based on position or previous terms.

- To find a rule for the general term it is often helpful to find the difference between successive terms.

- Two special sequences are: **square numbers**: 1, 4, 9, 16, 25, 36, ...
  'position rule' is square the position so the 7th square number is $7^2 = 49$
  'previous terms rule' is add the next odd number so the term after 49 is
  $7^2 + 8^{th}$ odd number = 49 + 15 = 64 (= 8^2)

  triangle numbers: 1, 3, 6, 10, 15, ... are found by adding consecutive integers from 1 or by the formula $T = \frac{1}{2}n(n + 1)$. For example,

  term 6 = 1 + 2 + 3 + 4 + 5 + 6 = 21 = $\frac{1}{2}(6)(7)$

Worked examples

Example 1

Simplify $3p - 2q + p - 5q - 4qp + 7pq$ by collecting like terms.

Solution 1

$3p - 2q + p - 5q - 4qp + 7pq$

$= 3p + p - 2q - 5q + 7pq - 4qp$ (Rearranging)

$= 4p - 7q + 3pq$ (Collecting like terms)

Example 2

If $T = 2a + 3b - c$ find the value of T

if $a = 7$ $b = -5$ and $c = -2$

Solution 2

$T = 2 \times 7 + 3 \times (-5) - (-2)$ (Multiply first.)

$= 14 - 15 + 2$ (Subtracting negative makes positive.)

$= 1$ (Think: $14 + 2 - 15$)

Example 3

Round biscuits cost r pence and square biscuits cost s pence. Write down an expression for the total cost of 8 round and 5 square biscuits.

Solution 3

Cost of 8 round biscuits $= 8 \times r = 8r$ pence

Cost of 5 square biscuits $= 5 \times s = 5s$ pence

Total cost $= 8r + 5s$ pence

Example 4

Simplify $6a^3 \times 3a^6 \div (3a^4)^2$

Solution 4

$6a^3 \times 3a^6 = 18a^9$ (Multiply coefficients but add indices.)

$(3a^4)^2 = 9a^8$ (Square the coefficient and multiply indices.)

$18a^9 \div 9a^8 = 2a^1 = 2a$ (Divide coefficients but subtract indices.)

Example 5

Find the 9th and 20th terms of the sequence 3, 6, 11, 18, ...

Solution 5

Find differences between successive terms: 3, 5, 7, ...

It is possible, but not efficient, to find 9th term by continuing the pattern.

It is better to use the sequence of square numbers: 1, 4, 9, 16, ...

Writing these terms underneath the given sequence shows we need to add 2 for the given sequence.

So 9th term $= 9^2 + 2 = 81 + 2 = 83$ and 20th term $= 20^2 + 2 = 400 + 2 = 402$

---

❶ Examiner's tips

- The rules in algebra are few and simple, but very precise, so take care over detail.
- Write clearly and check carefully, especially $+$ and $-$ signs and brackets,
  e.g. $-2 - 3 = -5$ *but* $-(2 - 3) = -(-1) = +1$
- Try to use the most concise form by collecting like terms whenever possible.
- Remember the sequence of square numbers: 1, 4, 9, 16, 25, 36, 49, ...
- Tabulating terms with working may help when analysing harder sequences.

Definitions

- **Arithmetic sequence** an ordered set of equally spaced numbers connected by the rule 'add a fixed number'
- **Square numbers** a sequence of numbers formed by squaring the position value of each term
- **Triangle numbers** a sequence of numbers from 1, formed by adding the next integer: 1, 3, 6, 10, 15, ...

Look on the CD for more exam practice questions

Can you answer these questions?

1. Simplify these expressions where possible.

   (a) $5x + 2y - 3x$ (b) $3m^2n + 2mn^2 + 5mn$

2. Find the simplification for the expression $\dfrac{a+1}{ab} - \dfrac{1}{b}$

3. If $a = 2$ $b = -3$ $c = 4$ find the value of

   (a) $b^2 + 2c$ (b) $\dfrac{bc}{a+c}$

4. A spider has 8 legs and a beetle has 6 legs. Write down an expression for the number of legs on s spiders and b beetles.

5. Simplify (a) $3x^2 \times 2x^3$ (b) $12a^5b^2 \div 4a^4b^4$ (c) $(10m^{-1}n^3)^3$

6. Find the value of (a) 11^0 (b) 3^{-3} (c) $\dfrac{1}{2}^{-2}$

7. Find the next 3 terms of the sequence 6, 9, 14, 21, ...

8. Find the first 3 terms of a sequence if the general term is $5n - 3$

9. Find the rule for the general term in the arithmetic sequence 10, 17, 24, ...

Key facts

- Measurement helps us to compare things, and to solve problems in real life. You need to know how to solve problems involving the measurement of: length, area, volume, mass, temperature, time, speed and density.

- The main system of measurement in Britain used to be the imperial system. Since 1971, we have been using the metric system, which is a decimal (base-10) system. We convert between the different units by multiplying by powers of 10.

- We use **scale drawings** and scale models to help us represent places and objects in maps, plans and models. You need to be able to convert scale measurements to find real measurements, and vice versa.

- You need to be able to solve problems involving **compound measures** such as speed and density. You also need to be able to solve problems involving areas and volumes of different shapes from their **dimensions**. See the formulae on page 90 of this book.

Definitions

- **Compound measure** measure involving more than one unit, e.g. km/h
- **Dimension** a feature of shapes and formulae: e.g. a line has 1 dimension and an area formula has 2 dimensions
- **Scale drawing** a plan or map in which all lengths are reduced by a given scale and angles are unchanged

❶ Examiner's tips

- You need to be able to convert between the different standard units. In the metric system, the names of the different units of measurement tell us by which power of ten to multiply the basic unit.

kilo (k)	hecto (h)	deca (da)	deci (d)	centi (c)	milli (m)
$\times 1000$	$\times 100$	$\times 10$	$\times \frac{1}{10}$	$\times \frac{1}{100}$	$\times \frac{1}{1000}$

- For the imperial measures, you need to know the relationship between the different units so that you can convert between them. Refer to the table on page 90 in this book.
- Sometimes you need to convert between metric and imperial measures. Learn the following approximate conversions to help you:

Metric	Imperial
2.5 cm	1 inch
8 km	5 miles
1 m	39 inches
30 cm	1 foot
1 kg	2.2 pounds
4.5 litres	1 gallon
1 litre	1.75 pints

Can you answer these questions?

1. An architect makes a model of a building she has designed. She uses a scale of 1 : 80

   (a) The front door of the building will be 2.4 metres high in real life. What is its length on the model?

   (b) The height of the model building is 18.75 cm. What is its height in real life?

2. The dimensions of a barn are 48 m by 18 m. Draw a scale plan of the barn using a scale of 1 : 300

3. The distance between a school and a sports field is 8 km. On a map, the distance between them is 16 cm. Work out the scale of the map as a ratio.

4. A group of friends run a 42 km marathon. Their finishing times are given below. Work out each person's average speed.

   (a) Brett: 6.5625 hours   (b) Siobhan: 6 hours   (c) Lance: 8 hours and 20 minutes

5. Mark drove the 220 km from Glasgow to Aberdeen at an average speed of 85 km/h.

   (a) Work out how long the journey took in hours and minutes.

   (b) If he had driven the first 100 km at 95 km/h and the rest at 85 km/h, how much time would he have saved?

6. The table below gives you the densities of some different materials. Use it to help you answer the questions that follow.

Material	Density in g/cm^3
Iron	7.86
Silver	10.5
Gold	19.3

   (a) A gold bangle has a mass of 23 g. Work out the volume of gold in the bangle.

   (b) The volume of a silver statuette is 228 cm^3. Work out the mass of the statuette.

   (c) A sheet of iron has a mass of 180 g. What is its volume?

   (d) Jenny makes a pendant out of one of the metals listed above. The pendant has a volume of 1.4 cm^3 and a mass of 14.7 g. Which metal did she use?

7. For each of the following expressions, write whether they express a length, an area, a volume, or none of these, and give a reason for your answer. (Note: the letters b, h and r represent lengths.)

   (a) $8bh$ (b) $2b(r + 25)$ (c) brh (d) $\dfrac{h}{r} \times 16r$

8. Express these quantities in the metric units given in brackets. Round off your answer to 1 decimal place if necessary.

   (a) 15 miles (km)   (b) 25 pounds (kg)   (c) 18 gallons (litres)   (d) $14\frac{1}{2}$ inches (cm)

9. Express the following quantities in the imperial units given in brackets. Round off your answer to 1 decimal place if necessary.

   (a) 20 kg (pounds)   (b) 128 litres (gallons)   (c) 448 km (miles)   (d) 78 cm (feet)

Did you know?

- The metric system is a decimal (base-10) counting system, but there are many other counting systems. For example, the ancient Babylonians used a base-60 system. We still use it in the way we measure time – there are 60 seconds in a minute and 60 minutes in an hour.

Look on the CD for more exam practice questions

7 Decimals and fractions

- The decimal point separates the whole number from the fractional number.
- If you multiply the numerator of an expression by a power of 10 (or divide the denominator by a power of 10) then the value of the expression is multiplied by the same power of 10.
- If you divide the numerator of an expression by a power of 10 (or multiply the denominator by a power of 10) then the value of the expression is divided by the same power of 10.

Definitions

- **Recurring decimal** has 1 or more repeating figures
- **Terminating decimal** has a finite number of decimal places

❶ Examiner's tips

- When you add or subtract decimals, always line up the decimal points first.
- When you multiply by a decimal, ignore the decimal point. Do the multiplication using whole numbers. Put in the decimal point afterwards.
- When you divide by a decimal, write the division as a fraction. Then multiply the numerator and denominator by a power of 10 to find an equivalent fraction with an integer as the denominator.
- You can convert a **recurring decimal** to a fraction like this.

Let $0.818181... = x$ (Let the recurring decimal equal x.)

$100x = 81.818...$ (Multiply x by 10 to the power of the number of recurring digits, in this case 2)

$100x - x = 81.818... - 0.818...$ (Subtract the equations.)

$99x = 81$ (Use the answer to find the value of x as a fraction.)

$x = \dfrac{81}{99}$

$x = \dfrac{9}{11}$

Can you answer these questions?

1. Order each set of numbers from smallest to greatest.

    (a) 0.251   2.001   0.02   0.2   0.225

    (b) 7.2   7.098   7.008   7.089   7.0099

2. Work out

    (a) 7.5 + 3.8   (b) 4.39 + 2.85   (c) 74.05 + 155.1

    (d) 442.3 + 8.97   (e) 7.38 − 1.22   (f) 68.72 − 43.9

    (g) 10 − 0.78   (h) 2.98 − 0.0631

3. Work out

    (a) 3.28 × 10   (b) 24.8399 × 100   (c) 0.0214 × 1000

    (d) 0.2 × 1000   (e) 4.6 × 2.3   (f) 0.87 × 1.2

    (g) 3.5 × 1.9   (h) 0.034 × 0.2

4. Work out

    (a) 49.95 ÷ 10   (b) 0.0778 ÷ 100   (c) 1.0118 ÷ 1000

    (d) 0.004 ÷ 10   (e) 18 ÷ 0.6   (f) 25 ÷ 0.2

    (g) 14.8 ÷ 0.4   (h) 0.0000868 ÷ 0.08

5. Given that 4.2 × 2.6 = 10.92 work out

    (a) 42 × 26   (b) 420 × 2.6   (c) 0.42 × 0.26

    (d) 0.42 × 26

6. Given that 10.8 ÷ 2.25 = 4.8 work out

    (a) 108 ÷ 225   (b) 108 ÷ 22.5   (c) 0.108 ÷ 0.225

    (d) 1080 ÷ 2250

7. Write these decimals as fractions in their simplest form.

    (a) 0.775   (b) 3.85   (c) 1.625   (d) 25.25

8. Write these fractions as decimals.

    (a) $\frac{4}{5}$ (b) $\frac{7}{8}$ (c) $\frac{5}{6}$ (d) $\frac{7}{12}$

9. Convert these recurring decimals to fractions.

    (a) 8.8181...   (b) 0.6363...   (c) 4.83333...

    (d) 0.923076923076...

10. Round off to the number of significant figures given in brackets.

    (a) 45.972 (1)   (b) 2.0518 (2)   (c) 0.01387 (2)

    (d) 670.00162 (3)

Expanding brackets and factorising

Key facts

- Expanding brackets is also known as multiplying out brackets.

- To **expand** something like $4x(x + 2y - 3)$ multiply each term inside the brackets by the term outside the brackets. This gives
  $4x(x + 2y - 3) = 4x^2 + 8xy - 12x$.

- Factorising is the reverse process of expanding brackets.

- To **factorise** something like $6x + 9y$ take the highest common factor, 3, outside some brackets and then put an expression inside the brackets so that they would multiply out to make $6x + 9y$. This gives $6x + 9y = 3(2x + 3y)$.

- To expand the product of two brackets, multiply each term in the first bracket by the second bracket. Simplify the result if possible. Here are some examples.

$$
\begin{aligned}
(x + 3)(x - 2) &= x(x - 2) + 3(x - 2) \\
&= x^2 - 2x + 3x - 6 \\
&= x^2 + x - 6
\end{aligned}
\qquad
\begin{aligned}
(2x - 5)(3x + 4) &= 2x(3x + 4) - 5(3x + 4) \\
&= 6x^2 + 8x - 15x - 20 \\
&= 6x^2 - 7x - 20
\end{aligned}
$$

$$
\begin{aligned}
(x + a)^2 &= (x + a)(x + a) \\
&= x(x + a) + a(x + a) \\
&= x^2 + ax + ax + a^2 \\
&= x^2 + 2ax + a^2
\end{aligned}
\qquad
\begin{aligned}
(2x - y)^2 &= (2x - y)(2x - y) \\
&= 2x(2x - y) - y(2x - y) \\
&= 4x^2 - 2xy - 2xy + y^2 \\
&= 4x^2 - 4xy + y^2
\end{aligned}
$$

- To factorise an expression of the form $x^2 + bx + c$ start by trying to find two numbers whose product is c and whose sum is b. For example, to factorise $x^2 - 5x + 6$ find two numbers whose product is 6 and whose sum is -5.

  $-2 \times -3 = 6$ and $-2 + -3 = -5$

  $x^2 - 5x + 6 = (x - 2)(x - 3)$

  Check that $(x - 2)(x - 3)$ multiplies out to make $x^2 - 5x + 6$

- An expression of the form $A^2 - B^2$ is known as the difference of two squares and factorises to give the product of the sum and the difference of A and B. In other words $A^2 - B^2 = (A + B)(A - B)$.

  To make use of the result $A^2 - B^2 = (A + B)(A - B)$ you need to be able to recognise the values of A and B. Here are some examples.

  (a) $871^2 - 129^2$ $A = 871$ and $B = 129$

  $871^2 - 129^2 = (871 + 129)(871 - 129) = 1000 \times 742 = 742\,000$

  (b) $x^2 - 25$ $A = x$ and $B = 5$

  $x^2 - 25 = (x + 5)(x - 5)$

  (c) $9p^2 - (2p + 1)^2$ $A = 3p$ and $B = 2p + 1$

  $9p^2 - (2p + 1)^2 = (3p + (2p + 1))(3p - (2p + 1)) = (5p + 1)(p - 1)$

Worked example

Factorise completely $10x^2y^2 - 15xy^3$

Solution

$10x^2y^2 - 15xy^3 = 5xy^2(2x - 3y)$ The highest common factor is $5xy^2$.

(If $5xy$ was taken outside the brackets instead of $5xy^2$ then this would give
$10x^2y^2 - 15xy^3 = 5xy(2xy - 3y^2)$ which is not factorised *completely*.)

Definitions

- **Expand (brackets)** multiply out
- **Factorise** break up into factors, write an expression using brackets, taking common factors out of the expression

Look on the CD for more exam practice questions

❶ Examiner's tips

- The factorised form of an expression should multiply out to make its original form.
- When the question says 'factorise completely', take particular care to find the *highest* common factor. As a check, the terms inside the brackets should not have any common factors.

Can you answer these questions?

1. Work out $9947^2 - 53^2$ without using a calculator.

2. Expand

   (a) $4(2x - 3)$ (b) $3x(4x + y)$ (c) $(x + 2)(x - 3)$

   (d) $(3x - 5)(2x + 6)$ (e) $(3x - 1)^2$

3. Factorise completely

   (a) $5x^2 - 10x$ (b) $12x^2y^3 + 8x^2y^4 - 4x^3y^3$

   (c) $x^2 - 8x + 15$ (d) $9x^2 - 16y^4$

9 2-D Shapes

Key facts

- Polygons labelled with letters at the vertices are named by using the letters in order around the shape.

- **Special quadrilaterals**

  A trapezium has one pair of parallel opposite sides.

  A parallelogram has two pairs of parallel opposite sides.

  A rhombus is a parallelogram with all sides equal.

  A rectangle is a parallelogram with all angles equal to 90°.

  A square is a parallelogram with all sides and angles equal.

  A kite has adjacent sides equal.

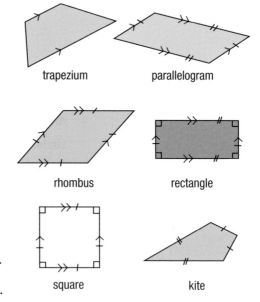

trapezium   parallelogram

rhombus   rectangle

square   kite

- All parallelograms have opposite sides and angles equal.

- The diagonals of a parallelogram bisect each other and the area, and in a square and rhombus they are at right-angles.

- Important length (1-D) and area (2-D) formulae are:

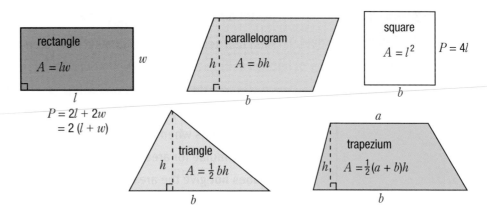

rectangle
$A = lw$
w
l
$P = 2l + 2w$
$\quad = 2(l + w)$

parallelogram
$A = bh$
h
b

square
$A = l^2$
$P = 4l$
b

triangle
$A = \frac{1}{2}bh$
h
b

trapezium
$A = \frac{1}{2}(a + b)h$
a
h
b

- In area calculations try to put all dimensions in the same units.
  Otherwise use these conversions: $1\,\text{cm}^2 = (10\,\text{mm})^2 = 100\,\text{mm}^2$
  $1\,\text{m}^2 = (100\,\text{cm})^2 = 10\,000\,\text{cm}^2$

▶ *continued*

Key facts

- Solving a linear equation involves 'undoing' operations like $+$, $-$, $\times$ and $\div$, using their inverses, to isolate the unknown variable.

- The basic rule for solving **equations** is *do the same to both sides*.

- It is better only to do things which help you solve the equation. Practice improves your ability to choose what is helpful.

- Some problems may be solved by forming and using linear equations. It is important to define the variable used.

- It is impossible to solve one equation with two unknown variables, so a second equation linking the same variables is needed.

- A pair of simultaneous equations is needed to find the values of two variables. Three equations would be needed if there were three variables.

- Solving simultaneous equations involves combining them to create a single equation with one unknown variable.

- One method is to change one or both equations, using multipliers, so one unknown is eliminated when they are added or subtracted.

Worked example

Example 1

Solve these equations. (a) $3x + 5 = 26$ (b) $5x - 2 = 7x + 6$

Solution 1

(a) $3x + 5 = 26$ (Read this as 3 times an unknown, then add 5 makes 26)

         $3x = 21$ (Subtract 5 from both sides to undo the last operation, +5, first.)

          $x = 7$ (To remove coefficient divide by it. Divide both sides by 3)

Check: $3 \times 7 + 5 = 21 + 5 = 26$ (correct)

You may find a flow diagram solution helpful.

Equation $\longrightarrow$ $\boxed{x}$ $\xrightarrow{\times 3}$ $\boxed{3x}$ $\xrightarrow{+5}$ $\boxed{26}$

$\boxed{7}$ $\xleftarrow{\div 3}$ $\boxed{21}$ $\xleftarrow{-5}$ $\boxed{26}$ $\longleftarrow$ Solution

$x = 7$

(b) $5x - 2 = 7x + 6$ (There is x on both sides so collect where there are most.)

        $-2 = 2x + 6$ (Collect x on right by subtracting $5x$ from both sides. Notice the -2 is unchanged.)

    $2x + 6 = -2$ (Reverse the equation as it's more familiar this way.)

        $2x = -8$ (Subtract 6 from both sides. Note that 6 less than -2 is negative.)

         $x = -4$ (To remove coefficient divide by it. Divide both sides by 2)

Check $5x - 2 = 5 \times (-4) - 2 = -20 - 2 = -22$

      $7x + 6 = 7 \times (-4) + 6 = -28 + 6 = -22$ (correct)

▶ *continued*

Example 2

Eleanor is twice as old as Rachel and Alison is 5 years younger than Rachel. The sum of their ages is 27 years. Find the ages of the 3 girls.

Solution 2

Let Rachel's age be r years.

Then Eleanor is $2r$ years and Alison is $r - 5$ years.

So $2r + r + r - 5 = 27$	(Sum of ages.)
$4r - 5 = 27$	(Collect like terms.)
$4r = 32$	(Add 5 to both sides.)
$r = 8$	(Divide both sides by 4)
So $2r = 16$	
and $r - 5 = 3$	

Rachel is 8 years, Eleanor is 16 years, Alison is 3 years.

Example 3

Solve the simultaneous equations $4x - 3y = 8$

$$8x + y = 2$$

Solution 3

$4x - 3y = 8$	(1)	(Label both equations.)
$8x + y = 2$	(2)	
$8x - 6y = 16$	(3)	((1) × 2 to make 8 the coefficient of x.)
$7y = -14$	(2) − (3)	(Subtract to eliminate $8x$.) (Take great care with signs.)
$y = -2$		(Divide by 7 to remove coefficient.)
Put in (2)		(y is easier than $-3y$ to work out.)
$8x - 2 = 2$		
$8x = 4$		(Add 2 to both sides.)
$x = \dfrac{1}{2}$		(Divide by 8 Note: 4 ÷ 8 is *not* 2)
Check in (1)		(Use the other equation to check.)

$$4x - 3y = 4 \times \frac{1}{2} - 3 \times (-2) = 2 + 6 = 8 \text{ (correct)}$$

Solution $x = \dfrac{1}{2}$, $y = -2$

Definitions

- **Equation** a mathematical sentence with '=' to show that two expressions have the same value

Did you know?

- CROSS + ROADS = DANGER is a correct sum with each letter representing a different digit (1 – 9). Can you find a solution?

❶ Examiner's tips

- Read an equation carefully.
- Keep things simple by collecting like terms or cancelling whenever possible.
- 'Undo' coefficients by dividing by the multiplier, *not* subtracting it.
- Always check that your solution fits in the equation.

Can you answer these questions?

Solve these equations.

1. $7a - 8 = 27$
2. $13 = 2c + 4$
3. $\dfrac{1}{4}x - 5 = 11$
4. $4y + 107 = 99$
5. $5p + 2 = 4p + 11$
6. $5n - 7 - n = 19 + 2n$
7. $3(2h + 1) = 5(h + 4)$
8. $2(x + 3) = 2 - (x + 5)$
9. $\dfrac{4m + 6}{3} = 7 - 2m$
10. $5 = \dfrac{2}{w}$
11. $\dfrac{5}{1 - k} = 6$
12. $\dfrac{3q + 6}{8} - \dfrac{q - 5}{4} = 3$

13. Solve these simultaneous equations.

   (a) $3a + 4b = 16$
   $2a - 4b = 9$

   (b) $4x + y = 19$
   $5x - 2y = 1$

   (c) $3p - 2q = 14$
   $5p + 3q = -2$

Key facts

- Qualitative data provides information that we can't express in numbers, e.g. people's beliefs or attitudes, whereas quantitative data provides information expressed in numbers.

- Quantitative data may be discrete (having a definite value, e.g. a shoe size, a score on a dice) or continuous (having any value, e.g. time, speed, weight).

- We can collect and record data in different ways: data sheets; tally tables (also called frequency charts); by experiments; in two-way charts; using questionnaires, and so on.

- Different sampling methods help us to ensure that our data is unbiased and representative. Some of these methods include random and stratified sampling.

Definitions

- **Class interval** the width of a class when data is grouped
- **Sample** a representative group of a larger group
- **Database** an organized collection of information

❶ Examiner's tips

- Whenever you present data, make sure that you label the table or graph. A graph should always have a title, as well as clearly-labelled axes.
- If you are listing items that are measured in specific units (e.g. hours, litres or kilometres) make sure you include the unit.

Can you answer these questions?

1. For each of the following, say whether the data would be qualitative or quantitative.
   (a) people's attitudes about a particular product
   (b) the percentage of the UK population living with HIV over the past 10 years
   (c) prices of different medicines
   (d) eye colour of pupils in a class

2. For each of the following, say whether the data is discrete or continuous.
   (a) weights of babies at a clinic
   (b) finishing times in a running race
   (c) lottery ticket numbers

3. Sally conducts an experiment to see how often she can throw a six on a dice. She throws the dice 20 times. Here are her scores.

2	5	6	3	4	5	2	6	1	1
6	5	4	3	4	2	3	3	6	4

▶ continued

(a) Draw a tally table to represent the outcome of Sally's experiment.

David does the same experiment. Here are his results.

3	3	5	1	6	6	2	3	6	4
4	5	6	4	5	6	1	5	5	6

(b) Draw a two-way table to represent both Sally's and David's results.

4. The following data shows the ages of the patients that visit a doctor's consulting rooms in a day.

(a) Use the data to complete the grouped frequency table that follows.

(b) Write down the modal class interval.

68	72	21	27	18	58	45	69	44	78	81	72	89	50
12	16	35	11	2	7	9	92	59	3	63	5	11	9

Age range (years)	Tally	Frequency
0–7		
8–18		
19–25		
26–40		
41–55		
56 and over		

5. A researcher is studying the amount of time people spend listening to the radio. She includes these questions in her questionnaire. For each question, suggest what is wrong with the question and give a better question that she could use.

(a) Do you agree that radio is a good source of information?

(b) How much time do you spend listening to the radio per day?

    1 hour   2 hours   3 or more hours

    ☐   ☐   ☐

(c) Which radio programmes do you prefer?

    Music   Talk shows   News

    ☐   ☐   ☐

6. Mohammed wants to find out how people feel about the cinemas available in his town. He plans to interview people outside the cinemas on a Saturday evening. Julia tells Mohammed his survey will be biased.

(a) Give one reason why the survey will be biased.

(b) Suggest one change that Mohammed could make so that his survey will be less biased.

7. You want to work out what percentage of pupils from your school have travelled abroad.

(a) Explain how you could select a random sample for this study.

(b) Explain how you could select a stratified sample from your school's class lists.

- Per cent means 'out of 100' and a percentage is a fraction expressed with a denominator of 100, e.g. $\frac{47}{100} = 47\%$

- We use an index number to give a measure of how a value has changed. We use 100 to represent the value in a given year, and base the index number on this.

Definitions

- **Multiplier** a number by which an amount is multiplied to increase or decrease the amount
- **Compound interest** interest based on the total value of an investment or loan at the end of each year

❶ Examiner's tips

- The inflation rate in a country was 3% one year, and went up to 4% the following year.

  Incorrect: The inflation rate went up by 1%.

  Correct: The inflation rate went up by 1 percentage point.

- For problems involving percentage profit and loss, make sure you know these formulae:

  $$\text{percentage profit} = \frac{\text{profit}}{\text{original amount}} \times 100\%$$

  $$\text{percentage loss} = \frac{\text{loss}}{\text{original amount}} \times 100\%$$

- Make sure you know how to use **multipliers** to calculate **compound interest**. You also need to use multipliers to calculate the original quantity when the final value after a percentage increase or decrease is known.

Worked example

In a sale, the prices of all the shirts are reduced by 30%. The sale price of a shirt is £33.95. What was the original price of the shirt?

Solution

Let the original price be x.

$0.7x = £33.95$

$x = £33.95 \div 0.7 = £48.50$

Can you answer these questions?

1. Express each of the following percentages as a fraction in its simplest form.

   (a) 20%   (b) 88%   (c) $22\frac{1}{2}$%

   (d) 10%   (e) 150%

2. Write each percentage as a decimal.

   (a) $19\frac{1}{2}$%   (b) 28%   (c) 50%

   (d) 99.5%   (e) 100%

3. Work out

   (a) 20% of 200   (b) 90% of 550   (c) 10% of 55

   (d) 25% of 88   (e) 9% of £38   (f) 6.5% of 350 g

   (g) 88% of 675 kg   (h) 18% of £480

4. 1200 delegates attend a conference. 804 of the delegates are men.

   (a) How many women attend the conference?

   (b) What percentage of the delegates are men?

   (c) 30% of the delegates were government representatives. How many government representatives were there?

5. Jackie bought a house for £195 000. She sold the house 5 years later and made 285% profit. What was her selling price?

6. Mike got 25 out of 30 for a class test. Work out his mark as a percentage and round it off to the nearest 1 per cent.

7. Sarah bought some beads, wire and other materials to make earrings. Her materials cost £18.00. She made 8 pairs of earrings and sold them for £4.95 per pair.

   (a) Did she make a profit or a loss on her earrings?

   (b) Calculate the actual profit/loss and percentage profit/loss that she made on the earrings.

8. £650 is invested for 4 years at 3% per year compound interest. Work out the total interest earned over the 4 years.

13 Graphs – including trial and improvement

Key facts

- Real life graphs can be straight, curved or irregular but conversion graphs are straight.

- Distance–time and velocity–time graphs show details of journeys.

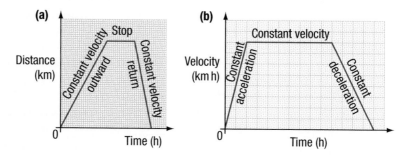

- In **algebraic graphs** the position of a point is measured from a fixed point (origin) so that the horizontal distance is its x-coordinate and vertical distance the y-coordinate.

- Axes are drawn and labelled for clarity. Here is an example.

  In the first quadrant the values of x- and y-coordinates are both positive.

  In the other three quadrants at least one coordinate is negative.

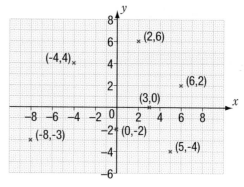

- For points on a straight line graph the coordinates are related by a linear rule such as $y = 3x$ as shown:

  The line may be infinitely extended to include points like (10, 30), (−4, −12), (200, 600). It also includes points like $(\frac{1}{4}, \frac{3}{4})$, $(\frac{1}{2}, 1\frac{1}{2})$, (2.1, 6.3)

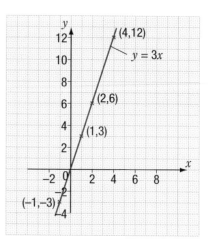

▶ *continued*

- Gradient (steepness) $= \dfrac{\text{change in } y}{\text{change in } x}$

- The multiplier (coefficient) of x in a linear rule fixes how fast y is changing compared with x and is therefore the gradient. Here are some examples.

  Graphs of $y = x$ and $y = -x$ have an equal angle of 45° to both axes.

  Steeper graphs have rules with coefficients numerically greater than 1

  Less steep graphs have rules with fractional coefficients less than 1

  Backward sloping graphs have rules with negative coefficients.

  For perpendicular lines, like $y = x$ and $y = -x$, and $y = \frac{1}{2}x$ and $y = -2x$ the gradient of one is

  $$\dfrac{1}{\text{gradient of the other}}$$

  Parallel lines have the same gradient and same coefficient of x.

- The position of a line is also affected by where it crosses the y-axis, called the y-intercept.

- The value of the y-intercept is added to the y-coordinate of all points and so is the constant term in the equation for a straight line. Here are some examples:

  - Graphs with a positive constant in the equation cross the y-axis above the origin and graphs with a negative constant cross the y-axis below it.

  - Graphs with no constant pass through the origin. These graphs are parallel because they have the same gradient and coefficient of x.

  - Graphs with no term in x are horizontal with gradient zero.

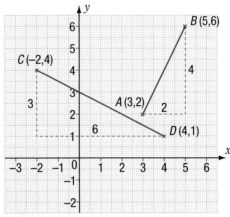

Gradient of $AB = \dfrac{6-2}{5-3} = \dfrac{4}{2} = 2$

Gradient of $CD = \dfrac{1-4}{4--2} = \dfrac{-3}{6} = \dfrac{-1}{2}$

CD has a negative gradient because it slopes backwards

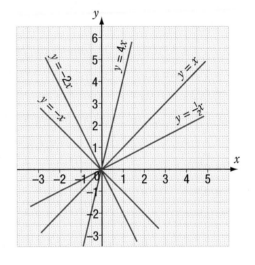

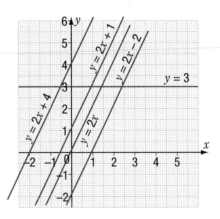

- Theoretically two points are sufficient for a straight line graph but it is better to plot three.

- The equation for a straight line graph is generally of the form $y = mx + c$ where m is the gradient and c is the intercept on the y-axis. Exceptions are lines such as $x = 3$ which are parallel to the y-axis.

▶ *continued*

- The straight lines for equations like $y = 2x + 3$ and $y = 6 - x$ have infinitely many points as there are many pairs of values which fit into each equation, but there is only one pair (1, 5) which fits both equations – found at the point where the lines cross.

  This is the graphical approach to solving simultaneous equations.

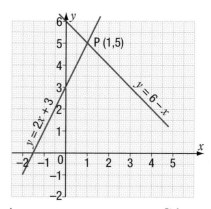

- Equations with index numbers produce curved graphs.

- **Quadratic graphs**, from quadratic functions (expressions) have line symmetry about an axis and are approximately U-shaped.

  This graph can be used to solve these equations.

  $x^2 - 2x - 3 = 0$, solutions are where the curve crosses the x-axis (A and B), $x = -1$ and 3

  $x^2 - 2x - 3 = 5$, solutions are where the curve crosses the line $y = 5$ (C and D), $x = 2$ and 4. This equation can also be written as $x^2 - 2x - 8 = 0$

  $x^2 - 2x - 3 = x - 5$, solutions are where the curve crosses the line $y = x - 5$ (E and F), $x = 1$ and 2 This equation can also be written as $x^2 - 3x + 2 = 0$

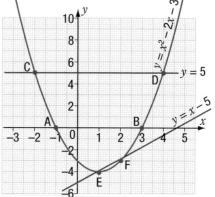

- **Cubic graphs**, from cubic functions, are S-shaped and some have rotational symmetry.

- Reciprocal graphs, from functions with x in the denominator, are sometimes symmetrical but do not cross the axes and are not continuous as there is no point for $x = 0$ or $y = 0$

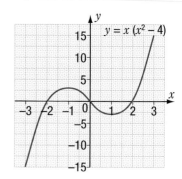

- **Exponential graphs**, from functions with x in the index number and a positive base number, do not cross the x-axis as negative index numbers make positive reciprocals, e.g. $2^{-3} = +\frac{1}{8}$.

  They cross the y-axis at $y = 1$ as $x^0 = 1$ They are useful in biology and geography as they illustrate cell division and population growth.

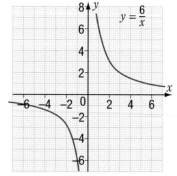

- Graphs can sometimes be used to solve problems. (See Topic 29)

- They can also provide an approximate solution to equations and then **trial and improvement** is used.

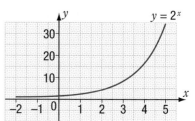

❶ Examiner's tips

● Always read the labels and markings on the axes of a graph.

● Label and mark axes on your own graphs, taking care at the origin.

● When calculating the gradient of a line joining two points use a sketch, especially if there are negative coordinates.

● Join points on non-linear graphs with a smooth curve.

Worked examples

Example 1

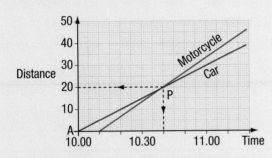

The two journeys shown on this graph are of a car which leaves A at 10:00 and travels at 30 miles per hour, and a motorcycle which leaves A at 10:10 and follows the same route at 40 miles per hour. What does the point P show?

Solution 1

The point P shows that the cyclist overtakes the motorist at 10:40, 20 miles from A.

Example 2

Solve the equation $y = x(x^2 - 4) = 10$

Give your answer correct to 2 decimal places.

Solution 2

Start by substituting single digit numbers.

For example,

$x = 1$ gives $y = -3$ which is too small.

$x = 2$ gives $y = 0$ which is too small.

$x = 3$ gives $y = 15$ which is too big.

So x is between 2 and 3

Use a calculator for remaining working and tabulate values, writing only 2 decimal places, to clarify thinking and minimise errors.

x	$x^2 - 4$	$x(x^2 - 4)$	Comment
2.5	2.25	5.625....	too small, so $2.5 < x < 3$
2.6	2.76	7.18	too small but nearer, so $2.6 < x < 3$
2.7	3.29	8.883	too small but nearer, so $2.7 < x < 3$
2.8	3.84	10.75	too big, so $2.7 < x < 2.8$
2.75	3.56...	9.79...	too small, so $2.75 < x < 2.8$
2.76	3.61...	9.98...	too small but nearer so $2.76 < x < 2.8$
2.77	3.67...	10.17...	too big, not so near

So $x = 2.76$ (correct to 2 decimal places)

- **Graph** diagram to show the relation between two quantities
- **Gradient** the slope of a graph showing how fast y changes compared to x
- **Cubic graph** curve from the cubic function $ax^3 + bx^2 + cx + d$
- **Quadratic graph** curve based on the quadratic function $ax^2 + bx + c$
- **Algebraic graph** graph with points based on an algebraic rule
- **Exponential graph** curve from the exponential function a^x where a is positive number and x is a variable power
- **Trial and improvement** the process of improving a guessed solution

Look on the CD for more exam practice questions

Can you answer these questions?

1. (a) Use the graph to convert
   (i) £10 to shekels
   (ii) 56 shekels to £
   (b) What is the rate of conversion?

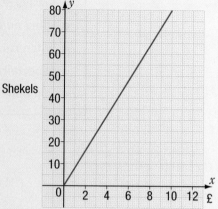

2. A man cycles for $\frac{1}{2}$ hour at 12 miles per hour, stops for 10 minutes to inspect a puncture and walks for 45 minutes at 4 miles per hour to a cycle shop. Draw a travel graph for this journey and find how long it took.

3. (a) Draw the graphs of $y = 3x - 4$ and $y = 6 - 2x$ using axes from −4 to 12
   (b) Find the solution to the simultaneous equations $y = 3x - 4$ and $y = 6 - 2x$

4. (a) Find the equation of the line parallel to $y = 5 + 2x$ if it passes through the point (0, 1)
   (b) Find the equation of a line perpendicular to $y = 5 + 2x$ and passing through the origin.

5. (a) Draw a graph of $y = x^2 - 5x$ for values of x from −2 to 6 and use it to solve (i) $x^2 - 5x = 0$ (ii) $x^2 - 5x = 6$
   (b) To solve $x^2 - 6x + 8 = 0$ you need to add a straight line graph. Find its equation.
   (c) Draw this graph on the same axes and solve $x^2 - 6x + 8 = 0$

6. Find, by trial and improvement, a positive value of x (correct to 2 decimal places) for which $x^2 (x + 2) = 5$

Did you know?

- Algebraic graphs use Cartesian coordinates, named after the French mathematician, Descartes (1596–1650). As he was a frail child he was allowed to stay in bed late and claimed as an adult that he did most of his important thinking during late lie-ins.

Key facts

- A transformation is a change in the position or size of a shape. You need to solve problems involving these kinds of transformations: translations, rotations, reflections and enlargements. You also need to perform combined transformations.

- A translation is also called a slide. We use **vectors** to describe translations for example, shape A is translated here by the vector $\begin{pmatrix} 3 \\ -2 \end{pmatrix}$ to make shape B.

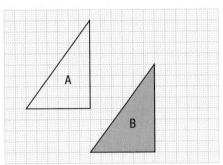

A translation
Shape A is transformed by the vector $\begin{pmatrix} 3 \\ -2 \end{pmatrix}$

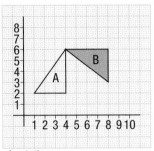

A rotation
Shape A has rotated 90° anticlockwise about the point (4,6) to make shape B

- To describe a rotation, give the angle of turn, the direction of turn (clockwise or anticlockwise) and the centre of rotation (point about which the shape turns). In a rotation, none of the following change: the lengths of the shape's sides; the angles of the shape; the centre of rotation. For example, shape A is rotated here 90° anticlockwise about the point (4, 6).

- To describe a reflection, give the mirror line. In a reflection, neither of the following change: the lengths of the shape's sides; the angles of the shape. The **image** is as far behind the mirror line as the **object** is in front of it.

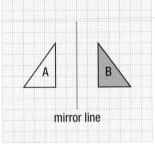

mirror line

A reflection
Shape A is a reflection of shape B
in the mirror line

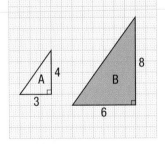

Shape A has been enlarged by a
scale factor of 2 to form shape B

- To describe an enlargement, give the scale factor and the centre of enlargement. The angles of the shape stay the same. The scale factor of the enlargement is the number by which the sides of the shape have been multiplied. If the scale factor is negative, the object and the image are on opposite sides of the centre of enlargement.

- Translations, rotations and reflections have no effect on lengths and angles. Enlargements change the size of the shape but do not affect the angles.

Definitions

- **Object** the starting shape for a transformation
- **Image** the result when an image is transformed
- **Vector** a quantity with magnitude and direction

❶ Examiner's tips

- When you work with vectors, the top number describes the number of units that the shape moves along the horizontal axis (left or right). The bottom number describes the number of units that the shape moves along the vertical axis (up or down). For movements to the right or up, use positive numbers. For movements to the left or down, use negative numbers.

Can you answer these questions?

1. To which kinds of transformation(s) does each statement apply?

   (a) The shape turns about a given centre point.

   (b) The size of the shape does not change.

   (c) It can be described by using a vector.

   (d) The object describes the shape before the transformation; the image describes the shape after the transformation.

   (e) This transformation changes the area of the shape.

   (f) The angles of the shape change.

   (g) This transformation is also known as a flip.

   (h) This transformation is also known as a turn.

   (i) It can be described by a scale factor.

2. Write the vectors for each of the following:

   (a) 5 units to the right and 3 units up

   (b) 17 units to the left and 8 units up

   (c) 12 units to the left and 12 units down

3. Rotate triangle A anticlockwise through 90° about the point (6, 7). Use graph paper to draw your solution.

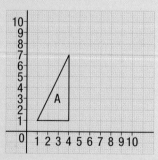

4. In the diagram on p41 describe the transformation(s) that would map:

   (a) triangle A onto triangle B

   (b) triangle B onto triangle D

   (c) triangle E onto triangle A

   (d) triangle C onto triangle B

▶ continued

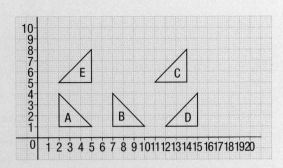

5. The diagram below shows shape F and its image, shape G, after a reflection. Draw the shapes on graph paper and show the mirror line.

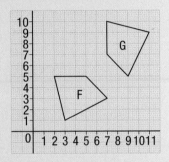

6. A rectangle has a length of 15 m and width of 6 m. The rectangle is enlarged with a scale factor of 3.5   Work out the length and width of the new rectangle.

7. The diagram below shows triangle P, triangle Q and triangle R.

   (a) Triangle P is an enlargement of triangle Q. Work out the scale factor.

   (b) Triangle R is an enlargement of triangle P. Work out the scale factor.

   (c) Triangle Q is an enlargement of triangle R. Work out the scale factor.

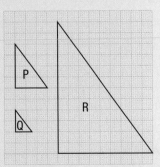

8. On graph paper, construct triangle XYZ using these coordinates:

   $X(5, 8)$, $Z(5, 2)$, $Y(1, 2)$.

   Enlarge triangle XYZ by a scale factor of −2 with the point (8, 5) as the centre of enlargement.

   Draw your solution and write in the coordinates of X_1, Y_1 and Z_1.

Key facts

- There are 4 **inequality** symbols. Here are some examples of their uses.

  (a) $a < 5$ means a is less than 5

  Possible values are $a = 4.99, 3.6, -2.5, -136...$

  Positive integer solutions are $a = 1 \quad 2 \quad 3 \quad 4$

  (b) $a \leqslant 5$ means a is less than or equal to 5

  Integer values include 5

  (c) $b > -3$ means b is greater than -3

  Possible values are $b = -2.99 \quad -1.5 \quad -1 \quad 0$ any positive number.

  Integer solutions are $b = -2 \quad -1 \quad 0, 1 \quad 2 \quad 3...$

  (d) $b \geqslant -3$ means that b is greater than or equal to -3

  Integer values include -3

  The range of values can be shown on a number line. Filled circles include 'equal to' values; open circles do not.

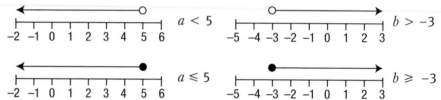

- Solutions to simple linear inequalities are in a range of values with one boundary value.

- More complex linear inequalities are solved like similar equations and involve more boundary values.

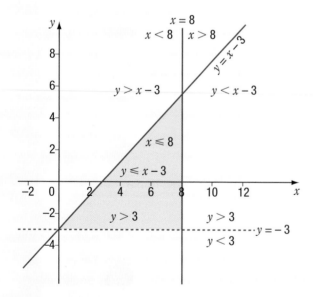

- Inequalities may be shown as regions bounded by graphs. A region includes points on solid lines but not dotted lines.

- For inequalities with '<' the region is below $y = c$, left of $x = c$ and generally below sloping lines.

- You can check you have found the correct region by testing the origin or the point (1, 1) or any point in the region. Here is an example.

  In the shaded region $x \leqslant 8, y > -3$ and $y \leqslant x - 3$

  Test (0, 0): $0 < 8$ but 0 is not $< 0 - 3$, so (0, 0) is not in the shaded region.

Worked examples

Example 1

Find the integer solutions to the inequality $5p - 4 > 31$

Solution 1

$5p - 4 > 31$ (Add 4 to both sides to undo -4)

$5p > 35$ (Divide both sides by 5 to undo $\times 5$)

$p > 7$

So $p = 8 \quad 9 \quad 10...$

Example 2

Solve $3 < 4x + 1 \leqslant 17$ and show the solution on a number line.

Solution 2

Write the two inequalities separately before solving. $\quad 3 < 4x + 1 \quad 4x + 1 < 17$

The first may be turned round provided the correct sign is used.

$4x + 1 > 3$	(Subtract 1 from both sides.)	$4x + 1 \leqslant 17$	(Subtract 1 from both sides.)
$4x > 2$	(Divide both sides by 4)	$4x \leqslant 16$	(Divide both sides by 4)
$x > \dfrac{1}{2}$		$x \leqslant 4$	

Solution $\dfrac{1}{2} < x \leqslant 4$ [Integer solutions are $x = 1 \quad 2 \quad 3 \quad 4$]

$\dfrac{1}{2} < x \leqslant 4$

number line: $-3 \quad -2 \quad -1\frac{1}{2} \; 0 \quad 1 \quad 2 \quad 3 \quad 4 \quad 5$

Definitions

- **Inequality** an open mathematical sentence which includes an inequality sign and so has more than one solution

❶ Examiner's tips

- Take care if reversing inequalities, e.g. $x > 2$ becomes $2 < x$
- Take great care with negative terms; using addition may help. For example, $6 - x < 4$ changes to
  $6 < 4 + x$ and so $x + 4 > 6$ so $x > 2$
  Multiplying by -1 is an option but carries risks; you must remember to reverse the inequality sign: $-6 + x > -4$, so $x > 2$
- In '$a < x > b$' and '$a > x < b$' either a or b is unnecessary. For example, $9 < x > 4$ means $x > 9$ and $x > 4$
  but $x > 9$ includes $x > 4$ which is therefore not needed.

Can you answer these questions?

1. What is the smallest integer solution to $x > -2.1$?

2. Solve these inequalities and show each answer on a number line.

  (a) $6x - 7 < 11$ (b) $3(x - 2) - 4 > 5$ (c) $7x + 3 \geqslant 2x - 2$ (d) $\dfrac{x}{3} < 0$

3. (a) Write down the equations of lines A and B in the diagram.

  (b) Find the gradient of line C and then write down its equation.

  (c) Write down 3 inequalities that define the shaded region.

4. (a) Draw graphs for $y = x + 2 \quad 3x + y = 5$ and $y = -2$

  (b) Shade the region defined by $y < x + 2$

    $3x + y < 5$ and $y \geqslant -2$

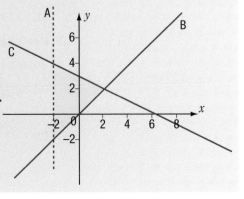

43

Key facts

- The digit with the highest place value in a number is the most significant figure (SF). 0 is not a significant figure, except when it is between two significant figures, e.g. 40 327 to 3 sf is 40 300

- When you carry out calculations with numbers that have been rounded, you can calculate the range of answers that may be produced, depending on the accuracy of the given numbers. You need to be able to identify the lower bound and upper bound of a given number.

Definitions

- **Estimate**
1) approximate amount 2) to calculate a rough answer using approximation to one significant figure

🛈 Examiner's tips

- A number that is 'correct to 3 significant figures' is a number that contains 3 digits that are not 0   For example, if you wrote the number 12.853 correct to 3 significant figures, the number would be 12.9
- A sensible degree of accuracy means give your answer to 2 or 3 significant figures. If the whole part of the number is large, give the answer to 2 decimal places.

Can you answer these questions?

1. Write these numbers correct to 3 significant figures.
   (a) 1748   (b) 19.86   (c) 0.4892   (d) 7.003088   (e) 1.03809

2. Write these numbers correct to 1 significant figure.
   (a) 150   (b) 1.9   (c) 11   (d) 27.8   (e) 8.97

3. Write these numbers correct to 2 significant figures.
   (a) 587   (b) 0.378   (c) 1.37   (d) 182.5   (e) 4573

4. Estimate the value of each expression by first writing the numbers correct to 1 significant figure.
   (a) 3.8×2.7 (b) 11.9×2.1 (c) 0.522×3.14
   (d) 9.15×0.6 (e) 764×2.9

5. Estimate the value of each expression by first rounding the numbers correct to 1 significant figure.
   (a) $178 \div 4.5$ (b) $995 \div 120$ (c) $476 \div 23$
   (d) $723 \div 14.8$ (e) $11.7 \div 1.6$

6. Use a calculator to work out the value of each expression. Write the answer correct to a sensible degree of accuracy.
   (a) $\dfrac{5.3^3}{9.48 \times 2.34}$ (b) $\dfrac{15^2 - \sqrt{15.8}}{12.3}$ (c) $\dfrac{\sqrt[3]{3.944\,312} \times 2.7^2}{23}$

   (d) $\dfrac{1.84 \times 2.3^2}{1.7^3}$ (e) $\dfrac{252 \div \sqrt{14.4}}{8.3^2}$

▶ continued

7. Write down the smallest possible mass and greatest possible mass of these.

    (a) a tin of peaches that holds 434 g correct to the nearest gram

    (b) a bag of oranges that holds 5 kilograms of oranges correct to the nearest kilogram

8. The diameter of a clock is 45 cm correct to the nearest centimetre. Write down

    (a) the longest possible diameter

    (b) the shortest possible diameter

9. Write the lower bound and upper bound of each of these numbers. Each number has been rounded as indicated in brackets.

    (a) 5.9 (1 decimal place)   (b) 7.83 (2 decimal places)

    (c) 0.317 (3 significant figures)   (d) 47 (nearest whole number)

    (e) 5450 (3 significant figures)   (f) 18.5 (nearest half)

10. When asked her age, Jenny says she is $9\frac{1}{2}$ years old.

    (a) To what unit has she rounded her age?

    (b) Give the lower bound and upper bound of her measurement in years and months.

Look on the CD for more exam practice questions

17 Averages and spread

Key facts

- You need to know about three types of **average**, the mean, the mode and the median.

- To find the mean of a set of numbers, add them all up and divide by the number of them. This may be written as

  $$\text{mean} = \frac{\text{sum of all the numbers}}{\text{how many numbers there are}} \quad \text{or as } \bar{x} = \frac{\Sigma x}{n}$$

  The symbol Σ is used to stand for 'the sum of'. For example, the mean of 3, 5, 9, 6 and 4 is $\dfrac{3 + 5 + 9 + 6 + 4}{5} = \dfrac{27}{5} = 5.4$

- The mode of a set of numbers is the number that occurs most often. The mode is sometimes called the modal value and there may be more than one for a given set of numbers. Here are some examples.

  (a) 4   5   3   6   3   7   4   3   6 has modal value 3 because 3 occurs more often than any other value.

  (b) 15   15   17   16   18   16   15   14   16 has modal values 15 and 16

- The median of a set of numbers is the middle value once the numbers are written in order of size. If there are two middle numbers then the median is halfway between the two numbers. Here are some examples.

  (a) To find the median of 5   3   9   7   6 they must first be written in order: 3   5   **6**   7   9

  This shows that the median is 6

  In general, once the numbers are in order, the *position* of the median is given by $\frac{1}{2}(n + 1)$

  In this case, there are 5 numbers and the median is in position $\frac{1}{2}(5 + 1) = 3$. The 3rd number is 6

  (b) The numbers 3   6   **7**   **8**   8   9 are already in order and the middle pair is 7   8. The median is 7.5

- You can find averages from a frequency table. Here is an example.

  A tetrahedral dice is thrown 20 times. The frequency table shows the scores.

Score	Frequency
1	4
2	7
3	6
4	3

▶ *continued*

The modal score is 2 since this is the score with the highest frequency.

The median position is given by

$\frac{1}{2}(20 + 1) = 10.5$ which means halfway between the 10th and 11th numbers.

From the table, the first 4 numbers are 1s and the next 7 numbers are 2s. It follows that the 10th and 11th numbers are both 2 and so the median is 2

To find the mean, it is useful to add an extra column to the frequency table.

Score (x)	Frequency (f)	$f \times x$
1	4	4
2	7	14
3	6	18
4	3	12
	$\Sigma f = 20$	$\Sigma fx = 48$

Σf is the sum of the values of f and Σfx is the sum of the values of fx. The mean is given
$$\frac{\Sigma fx}{\Sigma f} = \frac{48}{20} = 2.4$$

- An average is chosen to represent a set of values but gives no indication of how the values are **spread**. One measure of spread is the range which is the difference between the smallest and largest values. Here are some examples.

    (a) 100   100   100   (b) 0   100   200

    mean = 100   mean = 100

    range = 100 − 100 = 0   range = 200 − 0 = 200

    The mean is the same in each case. The change in the spread of data is indicated by the range.

- A problem with the range is that it is based on the extreme values of the data and so it may not reflect the true spread of the values in between. A more refined measure of spread is the interquartile range which measures the spread of the middle half of the data.

    The lower quartile is the value that is a quarter of the way through the data.

    The upper quartile is the value that is three-quarters of the way through the data.

    Interquartile range = upper quartile − lower quartile

- A stem and leaf diagram is one way to organise data in a visual way that makes it easier to find the mode, median and range. Here is an example.

    The number of e-mails received on one particular day by a group of 15 people were:

    21   16   3   12 9 8   15   27   16   11   34   28   33   8   25

▶ *continued*

Using the tens as the stem and the units as the leaves the data is represented as shown in the diagram.

```
0 | 3  8  8  9
1 | 1  2  5  6  6        Key
2 | 1  5  7  8           2 | 1 means 21
3 | 3  4
```

- A back-to-back stem and leaf diagram can be used to compare two sets of data. The common stem is placed in the middle and the leaves for the two sets of data are shown on the two sides.

- You can estimate the mean of grouped data by using the middle value of each class interval to represent the class.

- A moving average is worked out for a given number of consecutive values at a time. It may be used to describe the **trend** for the data.

Worked example

Find the interquartile range of

3 7 11 5 6 4 8 9 5

Solution

Write the numbers in order:

3 4 5 5 6 7 8 9 11

The lower and upper quartiles are in positions $\frac{1}{4}(n + 1)$ and $\frac{3}{4}(n + 1)$ with $n = 9$

The lower quartile is in position $\frac{1}{4}(9 + 1) = 2.5$
(halfway between the 2nd and 3rd numbers)

The upper quartile is in position $\frac{3}{4}(9 + 1) = 7.5$
(halfway between the 7th and 8th numbers)

lower quartile = 4.5   upper quartile = 8.5
interquartile range = 8.5 − 4.5 = 4

Definitions

- **Average** a representative value for a data set, i.e. mean, median, mode
- **Spread** how values in a data set are grouped about the average
- **Time series** a set of readings taken over a period of time
- **Trend** tendency of a graph of moving averages to increase or decrease

Can you answer these questions?

1. The mean of seven numbers is 11   When an eighth number is included, the mean is 10   What is the eighth number?

2. The table shows the number of online enquiries received by a website during its first six months of operation. Work out the 4-point moving averages for this information.

Month	1	2	3	4	5	6
Number of enquiries	47	83	142	116	157	170

Did you know?

- According to a survey by Google, people in the UK spend an average of 164 minutes online every day compared with 148 minutes watching television.

8 Formulae

Key facts

- A **formula** has a subject and an = sign followed by an expression. For example,

  $A = 2\pi r^2 + 2\pi rh$ is a formula for finding the surface area of a cylinder. (Each term involves two dimensions.)

- For a formula to make sense, all its variables must be defined.

- In formulae about shapes the variables often used for lengths are:

  l = length, w = width, b = base,

  a = length of side, h = perpendicular height, P = perimeter, r = radius, d = diameter, C = circumference.

  Formulae for area, A, and for volume, V, are given on page 90.

- Using a formula involves substituting given values for variables.

- Sometimes the variables have units but they are not used in the formula.

- Comparing the units on both sides can be used to check a formula.

- Sometimes it is helpful to change the subject of a formula. Use the same rules as for solving equations.

- These algebraic statements look similar but are different:

  $2l + 2w$ is an expression (like a phrase in a sentence).

  $P = 2l + 2w$ is a formula (a sentence with a subject, verb and object).

  $2l + 2w = 2(l + w)$ is an identity (two apparently different, but mathematically equivalent, ways of saying the same thing).

  $2l + 6 = l + 10$ is an equation (two different expressions using the same variable and having the same numerical value. An equation can be solved to find the value of the single unknown variable. In this equation $l = 4$)

- A **function** is an expression with one variable. For example, $f(x) = 2x$ is the 'doubling' function and so $f(3) = 6$

- Sometimes the expressions in related formulae may be combined to find connections between variables.

❗ Examiner's tips

- Check that formulae about quantities are correct by comparing units.
- When rearranging formulae with squares or square roots take great care with coefficients.

Worked examples

Example 1

A train travels at an average speed of 120 miles per hour. Find the distance travelled in a journey taking 3 hours 24 minutes.

Solution 1

The formula for finding average speed, s, is $s = \dfrac{d}{t}$ where d is the distance travelled and t is the time taken.

$s = 120$ miles per hour,

$t = 3$ h 24 minutes $= 3.4$ h (not 3.24 h!)

Substitute in the formula:

$120 = \dfrac{d}{3.4}$ (Multiply both sides by 3.4)

$d = 120 \times 3.4 = 408$

(Check units $\dfrac{\text{miles}}{\text{hours}} \times \text{hours} = \text{miles}$)

Length of journey $= 408$ miles

Example 2

The radius of a cylinder, r, is twice its height, h. A cube of length l has the same surface area, A, as the cylinder. Find l in terms of h and π.

Solution 2

$$r = 2h$$

Cylinder: $A = 2\pi r^2 + 2\pi rh$ (Area of two ends and the curved surface.)

$\qquad = 2\pi(2h)^2 + 2 \times 2\pi h^2$ (Remember $(2h)^2$ $= 2^2\, h^2 = 4h^2$)

$\qquad = 12\pi h^2$

Cube: $\quad A = 6l^2$

So $\quad 12\pi h^2 = 6l^2$

$\qquad l^2 = \dfrac{12\pi h^2}{6}$ (Divide by 6)

$\qquad = 2\pi h^2$ (Simplify by cancelling.)

$\qquad l = \sqrt{2\pi h}$ (Square root both sides so h^2 becomes h)

Definitions

- **Formula** a mathematical sentence with a subject, then '=' followed by an expression which describes a rule
- **Function** an expression, with one variable, for a rule that changes a number

Look on the CD for more exam practice questions

Can you answer these questions?

1. If $S = 3pq^2 - r$, find the value of S when $p = 2$ $q = -4$ and $r = 54$
2. A company sends letters costing m pence and packets costing n pence by post. What is the total cost, $£C$, for posting l letters and p packets?
3. Find a formula for the surface area (A) of a cuboid with dimensions a, b, c.
4. Rearrange these formulae to make the letter in brackets the subject
   - (a) $d = a(b + c)$ [b]
   - (b) $V = \frac{1}{3}\pi r^2 h$ [r]
   - (c) $y = mx + c$ [m]
5. Are these true or false? If false, write a correct statement.
   - (a) $A = 2b + C$ is an equation
   - (b) $mx + c$ is an expression

Did you know?

- Many people can quote Einstein's famous equation, or formula, $E = mc^2$ but do not know that E represents the energy of an object of mass m travelling with a speed of c, which is the speed of light (about 300 000 km/s).

Key facts

- Pythagoras' theorem states that in a right-angled triangle the square on the **hypotenuse** is equal to the sum of the squares of the other two sides. More concisely:

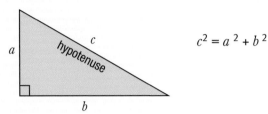

$$c^2 = a^2 + b^2$$

- Numbers in Pythagorean triples like (3, 4, 5) and (5, 12, 13) obey this rule and so using them may simplify some calculations.

- The converse (opposite) of Pythagoras' Theorem is also true. (i.e. if the sides of a triangle are such that the square on the longest side is equal to the sum of the squares on the other two sides then the triangle is right-angled.)

Definitions

- **Hypotenuse** the longest side, opposite the right angle, in a right-angled triangle

❶ Examiner's tips

- Before you use Pythagoras' theorem make sure you know where the right-angle is.
- Make sure the squares are added together before you find a square root.
- Remember that finding a shorter side involves subtracting squares of sides.

Worked example

Example 1

Find the length of the line segment *AB*.

Solution 1

$AC = 6 - 1 = 5$ units $BC = 5 - 2 = 3$ units

$AB^2 = AC^2 + BC^2$ (Using Pythagoras' theorem.)

    $= 3^2 + 5^2$ (Mentally add 9 and 25)

    $= 34$

$AB = \sqrt{34}$ (By calculator, but think: $6^2 = 36$)

    $= 5.83$ units   (Correct to 3 sf)

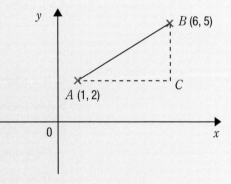

Example 2

A rectangle of length 13 cm has a diagonal of length 19 cm. What is the width of the rectangle?

▶ *continued*

Solution 2

Draw a diagram.

Diagonal = 19 cm   length = 13 cm

Let w cm = width   (Think: w is a short side.)

$$19^2 = w^2 + 13^2$$ (Using Pythagoras' theorem.)

$$w^2 = 19^2 - 13^2$$ (Mentally estimate $20^2 - 12^2$ as 250)

$$= 192$$ (By calculator – remember to press = button)

$$w = \sqrt{192}$$

$$= 13.9 \text{ cm}$$ (Correct to 3 sf)

Width of rectangle is 13.9 cm

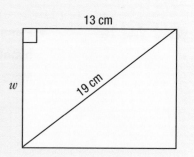

Did you know?

- Pythagoras was a vegetarian because he believed that human souls returned to life in animals.

Can you answer these questions?

1. Find LM.

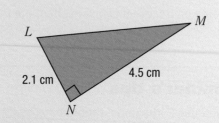

2. Write down the length of XY.
   Do not use a calculator.

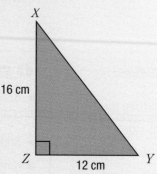

3. Find x in these right-angled triangles.

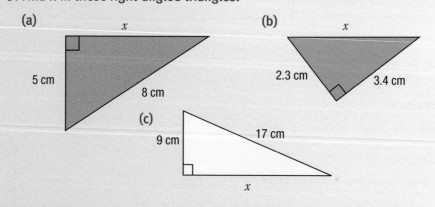

4. Is a triangle with sides 7 cm, 22 cm and 25 cm right-angled? Explain.

5. Calculate the length of a diagonal of a rectangle 12 cm by 13 cm.

6. A 4 m ladder leaning against a wall has its foot 1.6 m from the wall. How high does it reach?

7. What is the length of the side of a square with diagonal 10 cm?

① Trigonometry

Key facts
- Three ratios of length of the sides of a right-angled triangle, sine, cosine and tangent, are commonly used.

- Sides are labelled according to the position of an angle and ratios found as shown.

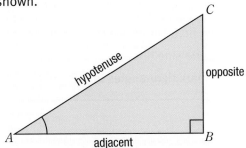

$$\sin A = \frac{\text{opposite}}{\text{hypotenuse}} = \frac{BC}{AC}$$

$$\cos A = \frac{\text{adjacent}}{\text{hypotenuse}} = \frac{AB}{AC}$$

$$\tan A = \frac{\text{opposite}}{\text{adjacent}} = \frac{BC}{AB}$$

- 'SOH CAH TOA' may help you to remember the ratios.

- All right-angled triangles with a second angle fixed are similar to each other and so the ratios of their sides do not change whatever the size of the triangle.

- When using trigonometry to solve 3-D problems you will need a 3-D sketch *and* 2-D drawings of sections.

- If triangles are **not** right-angled use the sine or cosine rules.

sine rule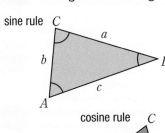

$$\frac{a}{\sin A} = \frac{b}{\sin B} = \frac{c}{\sin C} \text{ to find a side}$$

$$a \sin B = b \sin A$$

$$\text{or } \frac{\sin A}{a} = \frac{\sin B}{b} = \frac{\sin C}{c} \text{ to find an angle}$$

cosine rule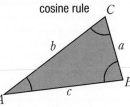

$$a^2 = b^2 + c^2 - 2bc \cos A \text{ to find a side}$$

$$\cos A = \frac{b^2 + c^2 - a^2}{2bc} \text{ to find an angle}$$

- Ratios for larger angles may be negative. For example, for obtuse angles, sin *A* is positive but cos *A* is negative. The diagram shows in which quadrants the ratios are positive.

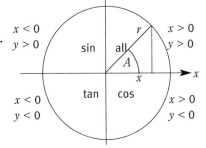

- Trigonometric graphs are symmetrical and repeat. Sine and cosine graphs are the same shape but out of step by 90°; the tangent graph has a gap at 90° and 270° because these values are infinitely large and undefined.

- If two sides of a triangle (*a* and *b*) and the angle (*C*) between them are given the area (*A*) can be found using the formula

$$A = \frac{1}{2} ab \sin C$$

Worked examples

Example 1

Cuboid *ABCDEFGH* has dimensions 8 cm by 6 cm by 3 cm. Find the length of its diagonal and the angle it makes with the base.

Solution 1

Draw a 3-D sketch of the cuboid with dimensions and any diagonal as they are all the same length. Add a diagonal in the base. Now draw any 2-D triangles that may be helpful: half the base rectangle and half the rectangle formed by vertical cut through the diagonal in the base.

Triangle *ABD* is right-angled at *A* so use

Pythagoras' theorem, with $AD = 6$ cm

As $8 : 6 = 4 : 3$ we know this is a 3, 4, 5 triangle.

So $BD = 5 \times 2 = 10$ cm

Triangle *HDB* is also right-angled with *BD* known

– mark on diagram – and $HD = 3$ cm

$HB^2 = HD^2 + BD^2 = 3^2 + 10^2 = 109$

$HB = \sqrt{109} = 10.4$ cm   (By calculator)

The required angle is marked in the cuboid and

as x in triangle *HDB*.

BD is the projection (shadow) of *HB*.

Triangle *HBD* is right-angled.

We could use any ratio but tangent is best because there is less likely to be an error in *BD*.

$\text{Tan } x = \dfrac{3}{10} = 0.3$ so $x = 16.7°$

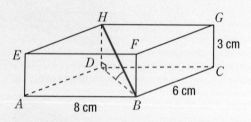

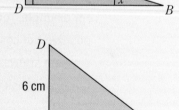

► *continued*

Example 3

Find the missing sides and angles of triangle *PQR*.

Solution 2

Check if the sine rule is appropriate.

Not appropriate since given sides not opposite given angle.

Use the cosine rule to find missing side *PR*:

$QP = 7$ cm $QR = 10$ cm   angle $P = 38°$

$PR^2 = QP^2 + QR^2 - 2QP \times QR \times \cos Q$

$ = 7^2 + 10^2 - 2 \times 7 \times 10 \times \cos 38°$ (By calculator, with great care)

$ = 38.68$ (Use 4 sf at this stage)

$PR = \sqrt{38.68} = 6.22$ cm   (Correct to 3 sf)

Now use the sine rule: $\dfrac{\sin R}{PQ} = \dfrac{\sin Q}{PR} = \dfrac{\sin P}{QR}$ (To find an angle)

Use the first 2 ratios because you know angle *R* must be acute as it is not opposite the longest side.

$\dfrac{\sin R}{7} = \dfrac{\sin 38°}{6.22}$ (Use stored calculator value for *PR*)

$\sin R = \dfrac{7 \sin 38°}{6.22} = 0.6929$ (use 4 sf)

$ R = 43.9°$

$ P = 180° - (38° + 43.9°) = 98.1°$ (Using angle sum of a triangle)

Did you know?

- There are three other trigonometric ratios called secant, cosecant and cotangent.

Look on the CD for more exam practice questions

Can you answer these questions?

1. Find *x*.

(a)
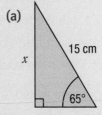

(b)
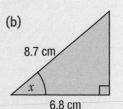

(c)
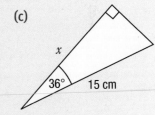

2. A boat sails from port 24 km east and then 15 km south. What is its bearing from port?

3. A 2 m pole is held vertically by 4 tight ropes tied to the top and fixed in horizontal ground at the corners of a square with sides of 1m. Find the length of a rope and the angle it makes with the ground.

4. Write down the positive or negative sign for

   (a) sin 100°   (b) cos 200°   (c) tan 300°

   Do not use a calculator.

5. In triangle *ABC*, angle $A = 41°$, angle $C = 56°$, and $BC = 6$ cm.
   Find the length of *AB*. (Hint: draw a sketch diagram)

6. In triangle *ABC*, $a = 8$ cm, $b = 10$ cm and $c = 14$ cm.
   Find the (a) size of the smallest angle   (b) area of triangle *ABC*.

Key facts

- **Ratios** are used to compare quantities.

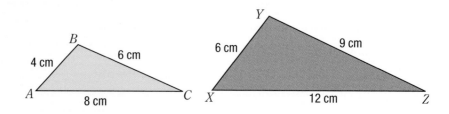

- The two triangles may be compared by looking at the ratios of corresponding sides.

    Sides AB and XY are in the ratio 4 : 6

    Sides BC and YZ are in the ratio 6 : 9

    Sides AC and XZ are in the ratio 8 : 12

- You can simplify a ratio in much the same way as a fraction, by cancelling common factors. Each of the ratios 4 : 6, 6 : 9 and 8 : 12 simplifies to 2 : 3 so corresponding sides of the two triangles are in the same ratio. This always happens with similar figures.

- The ratio 2 : 3 is in its simplest form because 2 and 3 have no common factor, apart from 1

- A ratio may be written in the form 1 : n by dividing both numbers by the first number. The ratio 2 : 3 is 1 : 1.5 in the form 1: n (dividing both sides by 2). In the diagram, this means that each side of the larger triangle is 1.5 times as long as the corresponding side in the smaller triangle.

- The order in which the numbers are written in a ratio is important. The ratio 2 : 3 is different from the ratio 3 : 2 for example.

- Ratios can be used to compare any number of quantities.

- Information from a ratio may be written as a fraction.

- A quantity may be shared in a given ratio.

- If two quantities vary but stay in the same ratio to each other then they vary in direct proportion.

- If two quantities vary so that as one increases, the other decreases at the same rate then they vary in inverse proportion. In this case, the product of the two quantities remains constant.

Worked examples

Example 1

Tom and Jerry share £36 in the ratio 5 : 4. How much does each boy receive?

Solution 1

$5 + 4 = 9$	There are 9 shares.
£36 ÷ 9 = £4	Each share is worth £4
Tom receives $5 \times £4 = £20$ 5 shares	
Jerry receives $4 \times £4 = £16$ 4 shares	

Example 2

The cost of rope is directly proportional to its length. A 12.5 m length of rope costs £10.50 How much would 7.5 m of rope cost?

Solution 2

12.5 m costs £10.50

2.5 m costs £2.10 (Dividing both amounts by 5)

7.5 m costs £6.30 (Multiplying both amounts by 3)

Example 3

It takes 4 men 3 days to harvest a crop. How long would it take 6 men?

Solution 3

The time taken is inversely proportional to the number of men.

$4 \times 3 = 12$	The job requires 12 man-days
$12 \div 6 = 2$	The job will take 6 men 2 days.

❶ Examiner's tips

- As a check, when sharing an amount in a given ratio, the shared values should add up to the original amount.
- When answering a question on proportion, establish whether the quantities are directly or inversely proportional.

Did you know?

- The frequency of vibration of a stretched string is inversely proportional to the length of the string.

Can you answer these questions?

1. Danielle and Kelly share a lottery win of £4200 in the ratio 7 : 5 How much does each receive?

2. On a map 5 cm represents 32 km. What distance is represented by 12.5 cm on the map?

3. A quantity of squash will fill 6 glasses of a particular size. A different glass holds 50% more. How many of these glasses may be filled from the same quantity of squash?

Look on the CD for more exam practice questions

Key facts

- We can use grouped discrete data to draw a **frequency** diagram. Frequency diagrams look the same as bar charts except that the label underneath each bar represents a group.

- We can use grouped continuous data to draw histograms. A histogram looks similar to a bar chart, but it has no gap between the bars. There is a scale along the horizontal axis rather than a label under each bar. We join the midpoints of the top of each bar to form a frequency polygon.

- Some information is better suited to a cumulative frequency table or graph. This gives us a 'running total' on amounts as they increase or decrease.

- We can use cumulative frequency graphs to find estimates for the number of items up to a certain value.

- Box plots (also called box and whisker diagrams) show the minimum, maximum, lower quartile, median and upper quartile of a set of data.

Definitions

- **Modal class** class with the highest frequency
- **Frequency** the number of occurrences of a specified outcome

❶ Examiner's tips

- Always use draw your graphs in pencil and use a ruler. Label all the axes.
- Remember the formulae for calculating the lower quartile, median and upper quartile of a range of data. For a large data set containing n values, read off the cumulative frequency axis at:
  $\frac{1}{2}n$ for the median $\frac{1}{4}n$ for the lower quartile $\frac{3}{4}n$ for the upper quartile.

Can you answer these questions?

1. A class of 20 students scored these percentages on their maths exam:

   85 84 78 56 65 72 92 58 65 88 72 67 68 49 38 80 71 79 55 60

   (a) Complete this grouped frequency table showing the frequency of the marks.

Test mark (%)	Frequency
31–40	
41–50	
51–60	
61–70	
71–80	
81–90	
91–100	

   (b) Draw a frequency diagram for this information.   ▶ continued

2. A company did a survey to see how many emails each employee sent and received on one day. The grouped frequency tables below show the results of the study.

Emails sent (x)	Frequency	Emails received (x)	Frequency
$0 < x \leqslant 10$	12	$0 < x \leqslant 10$	25
$11 < x \leqslant 20$	28	$11 < x \leqslant 20$	30
$21 < x \leqslant 30$	39	$21 < x \leqslant 30$	82
$31 < x \leqslant 50$	64	$31 < x \leqslant 50$	26
$51 < x \leqslant 70$	33	$51 < x \leqslant 70$	14
$71 < x \leqslant 100$	10	$71 < x \leqslant 100$	9

(a) Draw two cumulative frequency graphs plotting emails sent and received in the company on that day.

(b) Estimate the lower quartile and upper quartile for each graph.

3. The box plot below shows the results of a survey in which 120 people answered questions about how much coffee they drank per day.

(a) Write down the minimum value, maximum value, lower quartile and upper quartile shown on the box plot.

(b) The researcher concluded that 'Most people drink more than 5 cups of coffee per day'. Was she correct or incorrect? Give evidence from the plot.

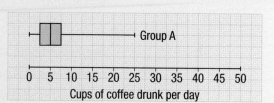

4. The histogram below shows information about the ages of people that called into an information helpline in an evening. Use the information in the histogram to help you complete the frequency table.

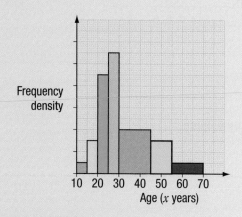

Age (x years)	Frequency
$10 < x \leqslant 15$	
$15 < x \leqslant 20$	
$20 < x \leqslant 25$	45
$25 < x \leqslant 30$	
$30 < x \leqslant 45$	
$45 < x \leqslant 55$	
$55 < x \leqslant 70$	

Look on the CD for more exam practice questions

Key facts

- When a plane cuts a **3-D** shape in two equal pieces so that each half is a mirror image of the other half, the plane is called a plane of symmetry.

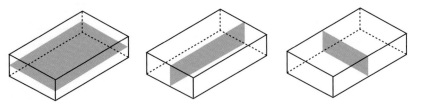

- The cross-section of a prism is the same all along its length.

- We can draw diagrams of 3-D objects from different points of view – from the front (front **elevation**), from above (**plan**) and from the side (side elevation).

- To locate a point in 3 dimensions, we use 3 coordinates: the x-coordinate, the y-coordinate and the z-coordinate. For example, in the diagram, the coordinates of A are (0, 3, 0), the coordinates of C are (0, 3, 2) and the coordinates of D are (4, 3, 2).

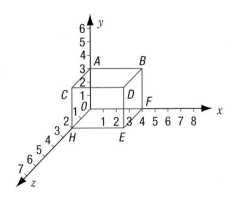

- We use cubic units for measuring **volume**.

---

❶ Examiner's tips

- The formulae for calculating volumes and **surface areas** of 3-D shapes are listed under Essential formulae on page 90 in this book.
- Always make sure that you are working with the correct units. When you calculate areas and volumes, make sure all the measurements are in the same units (i.e. don't measure height in cm and length in mm!)
- To change cm^3 to mm^3, multiply by 1000
  To change mm^3 to cm^3, divide by 1000
- To change m^3 to cm^3, multiply by 1 000 000
  To change cm^3 to m^3, divide by 1 000 000

▶ *continued*

Definitions

- **Plan** view of an object from above
- **Elevation** a side, front or back view of an object
- **3-D** solid, with length, width and height
- **Volume** amount of space taken up by a solid shape
- **Surface area** total area of all surfaces of a solid shape

Did you know?

- Scientists once developed cube-shaped tomatoes in order to fit more tomatoes into a crate or box. However, the packed tomatoes rotted very quickly because there was no air flowing between them.

Look on the CD for more exam practice questions

- Sometimes you may be asked to calculate the volume of a prism that looks different from those for which you have learned formulae.

  To solve these problems, construct a plane of symmetry that divides the solid into regular solids that are easier to work with. Can you see that shape A is made up of a cuboid and triangular prism; shape B is two cuboids and shape C is a cone and half a sphere?

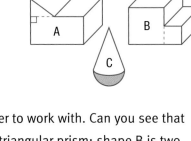

Can you answer these questions?

1. Draw a cuboid and show one plane of symmetry.

2. What would be the shape of the cross-section of each of these shapes?

   (a) a cylinder   (b) a triangular prism

   (c) a pyramid with base and four equal sides

3. Draw these views of a cylinder with radius of 2 cm and height of 5 cm.

   (a) plan   (b) front elevation   (c) side elevation

4. Draw a diagram to show the points A (0, 5, 3), B (4, 0, −1) and C (−2, −3, 0)

5. A box of biscuits measures 15 cm by 6 cm by 4 cm. A packing box measures 90 cm by 90 cm by 80 cm. How many boxes of biscuits will fit into the packing box?

6. Calculate the volumes of the following shapes. Note that the diagrams are NOT to scale.

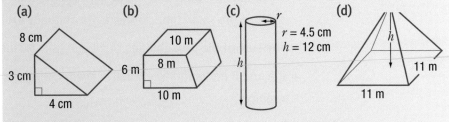

(a) 8 cm 3 cm 4 cm

(b) 10 m 8 m 6 m 10 m

(c) r $r = 4.5$ cm $h = 12$ cm h

(d) h 11 m 11 m

7. Change

   (a) 3700 mm³ to cm³

   (b) 0.88 cm³ to mm³

   (c) 1.8 m³ to cm³

   (e) 5 200 000 cm³ to m³

(e) $h = 19$ cm $r = 3$ cm h r

(f) $r = 8$ cm r

8. Calculate the surface area of the following cubes and cuboids.

   (a) a cube with sides of 8.7 cm

   (b) a cuboid with dimensions 18.5 cm × 12.5 cm × 10 cm

9. Calculate the surface area of a sphere with a radius of 14 mm.

10. The surface area of a cylinder is 565.5 cm³. The cylinder has a radius of 5 cm. Work out its height. Round to 1 decimal point.

Key facts

- An activity, such as rolling a dice, that may be repeated many times to produce a set of **outcomes**, subject to chance, is called an experiment. The complete set of possible outcomes of an experiment is called the **sample space**. For a standard dice, the sample space is 1　2　3　4　5　6

- An **event** is some collection of outcomes. For example, the event of obtaining an even score on a single throw of a standard dice has outcomes 2　4　6　An event may consist of a single outcome.

- The probability of an event, written as P(event), is a measure of how likely it is that the event will happen. It is given as a number from 0 to 1 inclusive, where 0 indicates that the event is impossible and 1 indicates that the event is certain to happen.

- When all the possible outcomes are equally likely

$$P(\text{event}) = \frac{\text{number of outcomes in the event}}{\text{number of outcomes in the sample space}}$$

- The sample space for an experiment may be represented on a **sample space diagram**. For example, the sample space for throwing two coins may be written as HH, HT, TH, TT.
The corresponding sample space diagram may be shown like this.

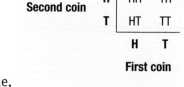

- Mutually exclusive events are events that cannot happen at the same time. For example, when rolling a dice, it is impossible to obtain an even score and an odd score at the same time so these are mutually exclusive events.

- The sum of the probabilities of all mutually exclusive events is 1.

- If A and B are mutually exclusive events, P(A *or* B) = P(A) + P(B). Here is an example.

  For a single throw of a standard dice it is possible to define mutually exclusive events in different ways.

  P(even) + P(odd) = 1　　　Any outcome must be even or odd but not both.

  $P(5 \ or \ \text{even}) = P(5) + P(\text{even}) = \frac{1}{6} + \frac{1}{2} = \frac{2}{3}$

- For some event A, if P(A) = p then P(not A) = 1 − p, where P(not A) is the probability that the event A does not occur.

- The relative frequency of an event is given by

  $$\text{relative frequency} = \frac{\text{number times the event occurs}}{\text{total number of trials}}$$

  Here is an example. If a coin is tossed 10 times and shows tails 7 times then the relative frequency of obtaining tails is $\frac{7}{10} = 0.7$

▶ *continued*

- The relative frequency of an event doesn't have a fixed value. For a small number of trials, its value may change quite erratically, but for a large number of trials, we would expect its value to be close to the probability of the event.

- If the outcomes of an experiment are *not* all equally likely then the method of calculating the probability of an event, given above, no longer applies. In such cases, the relative frequency of an event may be used to estimate the probability.

$$P(\text{event}) \approx \frac{\text{number of times the event occurs}}{\text{total number of trials}}$$

- A second result based on using relative frequency to estimate probability is

  Expected number of occurrences of an event = P(event) × number of trials

  For example, if the probability that a machine produces a defective component is 0.0017 then in a batch of 6000 components, the expected number of defective components = 0.0017 × 6000 = 10.2 ≈ 10

- Two events are said to be independent if the outcome of one does not affect the outcome of the other. For two independent events A and B,
  P(A *and* B) = P(A) × P(B). For example, if a coin and a dice are thrown together, $P(\text{heads}) = \frac{1}{2}$, $P(5) = \frac{1}{6}$

  The coin and the dice have no influence on each other, so the events are independent.

  $P(\text{heads and 5}) = \frac{1}{2} \times \frac{1}{6} = \frac{1}{12}$

- If the probability of an event depends on the outcome of a previous event, then the probability is described as conditional. For example, if event B depends on event A then

  P(A and B) = P(A) × P(B given that A has happened)

- **Probability tree diagrams** are a useful way of representing combined events.

  This is the probability tree diagram representing the random selection of two counters from a bag containing 3 red counters and 4 blue counters. The first counter is replaced.

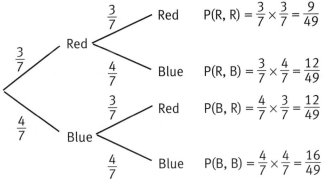

From the tree diagram, P(same colour) = P((R, R) or (B, B)) = $\frac{9}{49} + \frac{16}{49} = \frac{25}{49}$

Definitions

- **Event** a collection of outcomes
- **Sample space** complete set of possible outcomes of an experiement

---

❶ Examiner's tips

- You can use a probability tree diagram for combined events whether the events are independent or not.

Worked example

Example 1

A card is selected at random from a standard pack. What is the probability that the card selected is a diamond?

Solution 1

There are 52 cards in a standard pack.

13 of the cards are diamonds.

P(a diamond is selected) $= \dfrac{13}{52} = \dfrac{1}{4}$

Example 2

The probability that it will rain today is 0.3

What is the probability that it will not rain today?

Solution 2

P(not rain)	$= 1 - P(\text{rain})$
	$= 1 - 0.3$
	$= 0.7$

Did you know?

- The probability of winning the lottery jackpot is roughly $\dfrac{1}{14 \text{ million}}$ which is about the same as obtaining 24 heads in succession with a fair coin!

Can you answer these questions?

1. Find the error in the following argument.

   For a fair dice, P(odd score) $= \dfrac{1}{2}$ and P(prime score) $= \dfrac{1}{2}$

   P(odd score) + P(prime score) $= \dfrac{1}{2} + \dfrac{1}{2} = 1$ so the score is certain to be odd or prime.

2. A fair coin is tossed three times. What is the probability that it shows heads each time?

Look on the CD for more exam practice questions

Key facts

If a is any non-zero number then $a^0 = 1$ and $a^{-n} = \dfrac{1}{a^n}$

As a special case, $a^{-1} = \dfrac{1}{a}$ which is called the reciprocal of a.

Here are some examples:

$5^0 = 1$ $\qquad$ $10^0 = 1$ $\qquad$ $1.47^0 = 1$ $\qquad$ $\pi^0 = 1$

$2^{-1} = \dfrac{1}{2}$ $\qquad$ $10^{-1} = \dfrac{1}{10}$ $\qquad$ $5^{-2} = \dfrac{1}{5^2} = \dfrac{1}{25}$

$\left(\dfrac{a}{b}\right)^{-1} = \dfrac{b}{a}$

The reciprocal of the fraction $\dfrac{a}{b}$ is the fraction $\dfrac{b}{a}$ For example, $\left(\dfrac{3}{4}\right)^{-1} = \dfrac{4}{3}$

- Standard form is used to represent very large and very small numbers. A number written in standard form has the form $a \times 10^n$ where $1 \leqslant a < 10$ and n is an integer. Here are some examples.

$27\,000 = 2.7 \times 10^4$

Multiplying by 10^4 moves the digits 4 places to the left

$0.000\,003\,81 = 3.81 \times 10^{-6}$ $\quad$ Multiplying by 10^{-6} moves the digits 6 places to the right

264×10^5 is not in standard form because 264 does not lie between 1 and 10 However, it can be written in standard form by replacing 264 with 2.64×10^2 and then combining the powers of 10

$264 \times 10^5 = 2.64 \times 10^2 \times 10^5 = 2.64 \times 10^7$

- You can do calculations in standard form without using a calculator. Here are some examples.

(a) $(6 \times 10^7) \times (5 \times 10^4) = 6 \times 5 \times 10^7 \times 10^4$

$\qquad = 30 \times 10^{11}$ (This is not in standard form.)

$\qquad = 3 \times 10^1 \times 10^{11}$

$\qquad = 3 \times 10^{12}$

(b) $(3 \times 10^5) \div (8 \times 10^9) = \dfrac{3 \times 10^5}{8 \times 10^9}$

(The division can be written as a fraction.)

$= \dfrac{3}{8} \times \dfrac{10^5}{10^9}$ $\quad$ (The fraction can be rearranged.)

$= 0.375 \times 10^{-4}$ $\qquad$ (This is not in standard form.)

$= 3.75 \times 10^{-1} \times 10^{-4}$

$= 3.75 \times 10^{-5}$

(c) $(2.6 \times 10^7) + (3 \times 10^5) = (2.6 \times 10^7) + (0.03 \times 10^7)$

(Make the powers of 10 the same.)

$= (2.6 + 0.03) \times 10^7$

$= 2.63 \times 10^7$

▶ *continued*

- Calculations in standard form can be done on a scientific calculator. A typical key sequence for working out $8.72 \times 10^{14} - 9.6 \times 10^{13}$ is shown below.

| 8 | . | 7 | 2 | EXP | 1 | 4 | – | 9 | . | 6 | EXP | 1 | 3 |

This gives the answer in standard form as 7.76×10^{14}

- You need to understand indices expressed as fractions.

In general, $x^{\frac{1}{n}} = \sqrt[n]{x}$ and $x^{\frac{m}{n}} = (\sqrt[n]{x})^m = \sqrt[n]{x^m}$

Here are some examples

(a) $9^{\frac{1}{2}} = \sqrt{9} = 3$

(b) $64^{\frac{2}{3}} = (\sqrt[3]{64})^2 = 4^2 = 16$

(c) $25^{\frac{-1}{2}} = \frac{1}{25^{\frac{1}{2}}} = \frac{1}{\sqrt{25}} = \frac{1}{5}$

(d) $\left(\frac{27}{64}\right)^{\frac{-1}{3}} = \left(\frac{64}{27}\right)^{\frac{1}{3}} = \frac{64^{\frac{1}{3}}}{27^{\frac{1}{3}}} = \frac{4}{3}$

- A surd is a root of a number that cannot be written down exactly. For example, $\sqrt{4} = 2$ which is exact and so $\sqrt{4}$ is not a surd, whereas $\sqrt{2} = 1.41421356...$ is an **irrational number** so $\sqrt{2}$ is a surd.

In general, $\sqrt{(ab)} = \sqrt{a} \times \sqrt{b}$ and this allows some surds to be simplified. For example,

$\sqrt{12} = \sqrt{(4 \times 3)} = \sqrt{4} \times \sqrt{3} = 2\sqrt{3}$

Definitions

- Irrational number cannot be expressed as a ratio of integers

Did you know?

- A light-year is the distance that light travels in a year. This is 9.46×10^{15} metres.

Look on the CD for more exam practice questions

❶ Examiner's tips

- You may need to do calculations in standard form on the non-calculator paper.
- You may also need to use a calculator for standard form, so it is important that you are familiar with the key sequences necessary for your specific calculator. Some calculators use a [EXP] [× 10^x] [EE] key to enter standard form, depending on the make and model.
- When using your calculator, take care to interpret the display correctly and write your answer in the correct notation – some calculators will display 7.76^{+14} for example, to mean 7.76×10^{14}

Can you answer these questions?

1. Simplify
   (a) 2^{-3}
   (b) $\left(\frac{1}{5}\right)^{-1}$
   (c) $\left(\frac{25}{36}\right)^{\frac{1}{2}}$

2. Write in standard form
   (a) 123 000
   (b) 0.000 0047
   (c) 56×10^6
   (d) 0.024×10^{-5}

3. Simplify $\sqrt{162}$

6 Constructions, loci and congruence

Key facts

- Constructions are drawn with ruler and compasses only.

- To construct a triangle with sides of given lengths mark one length on a straight line and use a pair of compasses to mark the other two lengths, drawing arcs which cross to mark the third vertex.

- The locus of points a fixed distance, d, from a given point, A, is a circle with centre A and radius d. The locus of points less than d cm from A is the space inside the circle.

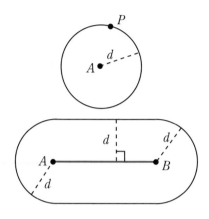

- The locus of points a fixed distance, d, from an infinite line is two lines, one on each side of the given line. If the given line, AB, is finite, the lines on each side are joined by semicircles with centres A and B and radius d.

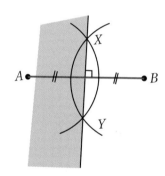

- Some constructions and loci are closely linked. Here are two examples.

  (a) The perpendicular bisector of AB is constructed by joining two points where circles, of equal radius and with centres A and B, intersect. The locus of points equidistant from two given points is the perpendicular bisector of the line joining the points. The locus of points nearer to A is the shaded area.

  X and Y are equidistant from A and B.
  XY is the perpendicular bisector of AB.

  (b) An angle bisector is constructed by drawing arcs to mark points equidistant from the arms of the angle. The locus of points equidistant from two intersecting lines, AB and AC, is the bisector of the angle formed by the lines. The locus of points further from AB is the shaded area.

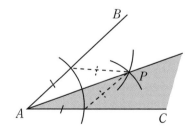

  P is equidistant from AB and AC.
  AP is the bisector of angle BAC.
  P

▶ continued

- A perpendicular may be dropped from a point to a line as shown.

  Draw an arc, centre *P*, to find *X* and *Y*.
  Draw arcs with centres *X* and *Y* to find *Z*.

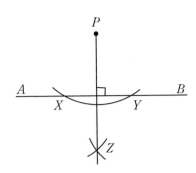

- A perpendicular to a line may be drawn by bisecting the straight angle formed at any point on the line, extending the line if needed.

- A regular polygon may be drawn inside a circle by dividing the angle at the centre by the number of sides. For an octagon the angle at the centre is 45° which can be constructed by bisecting an angle of 90°

- Finding **congruent** triangles is a key aspect of proving many geometrical facts, such as why these constructions work.

- A pair of congruent triangles has 6 equal sides and angles but it is sufficient to find only 3 pairs. These minimum data sets define a particular triangle and so form a condition for triangles to be congruent.

  The 4 **conditions for congruent triangles** are very useful:
  2 sides and the included angle (SAS)
  3 sides (SSS)
  1 side and 2 angles (ASA or AAS)
  right-angle, hypotenuse, side (RHS)

  Generally ASS is *not* a condition but RHS is a special case of this as the third side can be found using Pythagoras' theorem and so is equivalent to SSS.

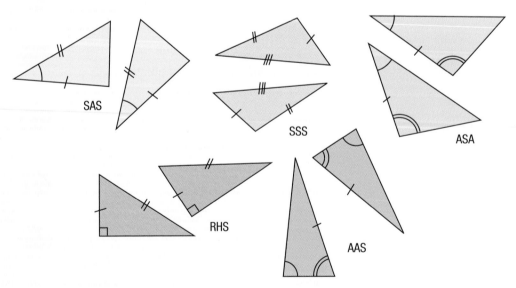

- When using congruent triangles in proofs select triangles carefully and find three pairs of sides or angles according to the above conditions. It is helpful to separate statements from reasons clearly.

Worked examples

Example 1

Construct an angle of 60°.

Solution 1

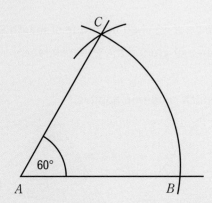

Draw a line and mark a point *A*, near one end as the exact end of a line is unclear. Use any convenient radius for the first arc, centre *A*, as the sides of the equilateral triangle can be any length. Keep the same radius to draw the second arc, centre *B*, where the first arc crossed the line. The point, *C*, where the arcs cross is the third vertex of the triangle. Joining *AC* or *BC* gives an angle of 60°

Example 2

Use congruent triangles to prove that the perpendicular bisector of *AB* is the locus of points equidistant from *A* and *B*.

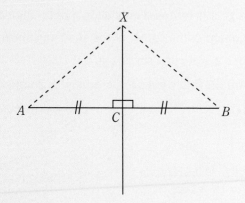

Solution 2

Proof

In triangles *AXC* and *BXC*   (Think: 3 statements with reasons needed.)

1   $AC = CB$ (Given *C* is the midpoint of *AB*.)

2   angle *XCA* = angle *XCB* = 90°
                    (Given *XY* perpendicular to *AB*.)

3   *XC* is common   (In both triangles)

So triangles *AXC* and *BXC* are congruent (SAS)

So *AX* = *BX*   (matching sides)

Definitions

- **Locus** path traced out by a point moving under a given rule, or the set of points obeying a given rule
- **Congruent** shapes have exactly the same shape and size

❶ Examiner's tips

- Make sure you have drawing equipment, with sharp pencils, a ruler, pair of compasses and protractor, for the exam.
- Do not use a protractor for angles in questions which ask for construction.
- Examiners can tell if you have used a protractor or not used a pair of compasses!
- For constructions, leave in arcs or construction lines. This increases the chance of gaining marks if you have made any mistakes.

Can you answer these questions?

1. Construct angles of 30° and 135°.

2. Construct a triangle with sides 9 cm, 12 cm, and 15 cm. What type of triangle is it? Prove your answer.

3. Construct a square with a diagonal of 10 cm.

4. A goat is tethered outside to a right-angled corner of a large (> 8 m) shed by a rope of length 8 m. Construct the corner of the shed and show by shading the area of ground the goat can reach. Use a scale of 1 cm to 1 m.

5. Are the following pairs of triangles congruent? If so, state which condition applies.

(a)

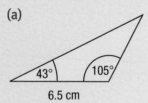 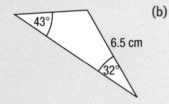

(b)

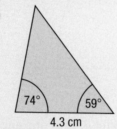 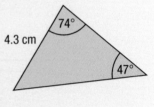

6. Given that triangle *ABC* is isosceles with *AC = AB* and *P* and *Q* on *BC* so that *BP = CQ* copy and complete this proof that triangle *APQ* is isosceles.

In triangles *ABP* and ….

1 *BP* = …..   (given)

2 *AB* = …..   (…………………………)

3 angle *ABP* = angle *ACQ*   (……………………………)

   So triangles *APB* and …… are …………………   (…………….)

So ……….. = ………..   (matching sides)

i.e. ………………………….

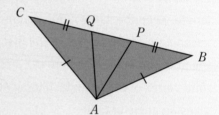

Did you know?

- Not all converses are true. Congruent triangles have all corresponding angles equal but if all the corresponding angles are equal the triangles are not necessarily congruent. (They are similar.)

Key facts

- The expression $ax^2 + bx + c$ can be factorised as $(px + q)(rx + s)$ if p, q, r and s are integers and

$$pr = a, \; qs = c, \; ps + qr = b$$

- As the numbers in questions are usually small, the number of potential solutions is not great. Practice improves chances of success.

- For quadratic expressions with "−" put the signs in the brackets first if possible.

- To simplify an algebraic fraction, factorise and cancel where possible.

- To combine algebraic fractions, factorise denominators if possible then find a common denominator.

- The **identity** $x^2 + bx + c = (x + p)^2 + q$, where $p = \frac{1}{2}b$ and $q = c - (\frac{1}{2}b)^2$, is found by completing the square. For example,

$$x^2 - 8x + 3 = (x - 4)^2 - 16 + 3 = (x - 4)^2 - 13$$

So the least value of $x^2 - 8x + 3$ is -13 and is when $(x - 4) = 0$ $(x = 4)$

- Algebraic proof uses the rules for algebra in Topic 5 (on page 16).

Definitions

- **Identity** two apparently different, but mathematically equivalent, ways of expressing the same rule

❶ Examiner's tips

- Place brackets round binomials in fractions.
- Always collect like terms and check for cancelling.

Worked example

Example 1

Factorise $6x^2 + 19x + 10$

Solution 1

Write

$(.... x + ...)(.... x + ...)$

with space for trial values to be written in pencil until confirmed correct.

$6 = 3 \times 2 \quad 2 \times 3 \quad 6 \times 1 \quad 1 \times 6$ and

$10 = 5 \times 2 \quad 2 \times 5 \quad 10 \times 1 \quad 1 \times 10$

Try $(x + 10)(6x + 1) = 6x^2 + x + 60x + 10 = 6x^2 + 19x + 10$ (incorrect).

Reversing 10 and 1 or $6x$ and $10x$ gives a factor divisible by 2 (incorrect).

$(3x + 5)(2x + 2)$ is also incorrect as the second factor is divisible by 2

Reverse the 2 and 5 or $3x$ and $2x$.

$(3x + 2)(2x + 5) = 6x^2 + 4x + 15x + 10$

$= 6x^2 + 19x + 10$ (correct)

Example 2

Simplify $\dfrac{x^2 - 4}{x^2 + x - 6}$

Solution 2

$(x^2 - 4) = (x + 2)(x - 2)$ (Difference of 2 squares)

$(x^2 + x - 6) = (x + 3)(x - 2)$

$\dfrac{x^2 - 4}{x^2 + x - 6} = \dfrac{(x + 2)\,\cancel{(x - 2)}}{(x + 3)\,\cancel{(x - 2)}} = \dfrac{x + 2}{x + 3}$ (cancel by $(x - 2)$.)

Example 3

Simplify $\dfrac{2}{x + 2y} - \dfrac{x - 6y}{x^2 - 4y}$

Solution 3

$x^2 - 4y^2 = (x + 2y)(x - 2y)$ (Difference of 2 squares.)

This is the common denominator.

Numerator $= 2(x - 2y) - (x - 6y) = 2x - 4y - x + 6y = x + 2y$

$\dfrac{2}{x + 2y} - \dfrac{x - 6y}{x^2 - 4y} = \dfrac{\cancel{x + 2y}}{\cancel{(x + 2y)}\,(x - 2y)} = \dfrac{1}{x - 2y}$ cancel by $(x + 2y)$

Example 4

Prove that the sum of 3 consecutive integers is divisible by 3

Solution 4

Let the numbers be n, $n + 1$ and $n + 2$

Sum $= n + n + 1 + n + 2 = 3n + 3 = 3(n + 1)$

Did you know?

- Although there is an algebraic proof that the product of three consecutive integers has a factor of 6 this non-algebraic proof is better: in a set of three consecutive integers at least one is an even number and one a multiple of 3 so the product has a factor of 2×3 ($= 6$)

Can you answer these questions?

1. Factorise

   (a) $3x^2 + 16x + 5$ (b) $2x^2 + 11x - 21$ (c) $14x^2 - 13x + 3$

2. Simplify (a) $\dfrac{2}{3x} + \dfrac{5}{2x}$ (b) $\dfrac{2}{2x - 3} - \dfrac{3}{3x - 2}$

3. Express in the form $(x + a)^2 + b$

   (a) $x^2 + 10x + 17$ (b) $2x^2 - 12x + 4$ (Hint: First write as $2(.....)$)

   (c) Write down the least value of $x^2 + 10x + 7$ and the corresponding value of x.

4. Find the mistake in this proof. Give reasons.

   If $a = b$ then $ab = b^2$

   then $ab - a^2 = b^2 - a^2$

   and $a(b - a) = (b + a)(b - a)$

   so $a = b + a$

   $= a + a$

   i.e. $a = 2a$

   so $1 = 2!$

5. Prove that the sum of 5 consecutive integers is a multiple of 5

6. Use algebra to prove the result about square numbers shown in Topic 5, page 16.

8 Circle geometry

Key facts

● The parts of a circle are shown in these diagrams.

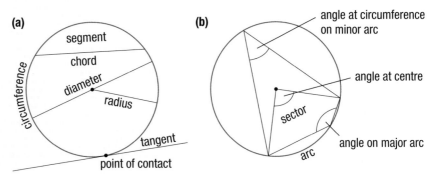

(a) segment, chord, diameter, radius, circumference, tangent, point of contact

(b) angle at circumference on minor arc, angle at centre, sector, angle on major arc, arc

● There are four basic circle geometry facts to which others are linked.

Fact 1 A tangent to a circle is perpendicular to the radius at the point of contact. (This can be proved by contradiction.)

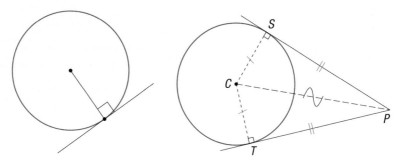

Deduction 1 The 2 tangents from a point to a circle are equal. Triangles congruent (SSS).

Fact 2 An angle at the centre of a circle is equal to twice any angle at the circumference which stands on the same arc.

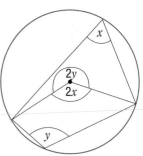

Deduction 2

(a) All angles at the circumference which stand on the same arc are equal.

(b) The angle in a semicircle is a right-angle.

(c) Opposite angles of a cyclic quadrilateral are supplementary.

(d) The exterior angle of a cyclic quadrilateral equals the interior opposite angle.

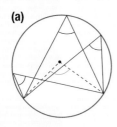

(a)

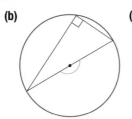

(b)

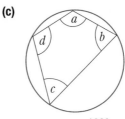

(c)

$a + c = 180°$
$b + d = 180°$

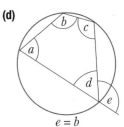

(d)

$e = b$

▶ continued

Fact 3 The angle between a chord and tangent equals any angle in the alternate segment.

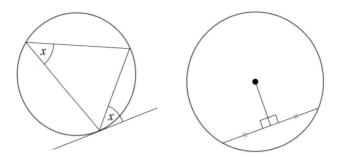

Fact 4 A line from the centre of a circle perpendicular to the chord bisects the chord

Worked example

Example 1

Given that *TQ* = *TR* calculate the sizes of the angles with letters.

Give reasons.

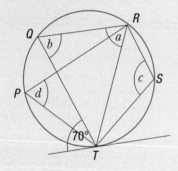

Example 2

In this diagram *C* is the centre of the circle, *PT* is a tangent to the circle and *M* is the midpoint of chord *PA*. Name all the right-angles in the diagram. Give reasons.

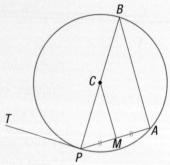

Solution 1

a = 70°	(Angle in the alternate segment.)
b = 70°	(Base angles of isosceles triangle.)
c = 110°	(Opposite angles of cyclic quadrilateral.)
d = 70°	(Angles in the same segment.)

Solution 2

angle *CPT* = 90°   (Tangent is perpendicular to the radius.)

angle *PAB* = 90°   (Angle in a semicircle.)

angle *CMA* = 90°

and angle *CMP* = 90° (*CM* bisects and so is perpendicular to chord *AP*.)

❶ Examiner's tips

- Do not assume that lines which cross inside a circle do so at the centre unless this is made clear in the question.
- Remembering the angle in a semicircle is important but be careful not to assume angles at the circumference are 90° unless it is clear they stand on a diameter.
- Turning diagrams upside down may help in looking for related angles.
- Add the sizes of angles to the diagram as you find them.

Can you answer these questions?

1. Find the angles marked with letters in these diagrams. Give reasons.

(a)   (b)   (c)   (d)

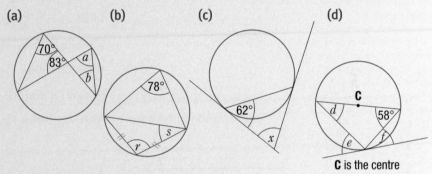

C is the centre

2. A point P is 10 cm from a point C which is the centre of a circle radius 4 cm. Calculate the length of the tangent to the circle from P. (You will need to sketch a diagram.)

3. Prove fact 2 by using the isosceles triangles in this diagram to find connections between angles a and x and between y and b.

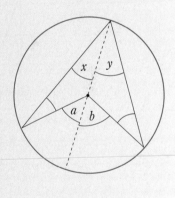

4.

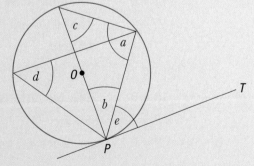

O is the centre of the circle and PT is a tangent

(a) Write down the value of a. Give a reason.

(b) Find e, c and d in terms of b. Give reasons.

Key facts

- Any quadratic equation can be written in the form $ax^2 + bx + c = 0$ where a, b and c are numbers and $a \neq 0$. A quadratic equation may have two solutions, one solution or no solution. Here are some examples.

  (a) $\qquad 2x^2 = 18$ $\qquad$ This could be put in the form $ax^2 + bx + c = 0$ with $a = 2$ $b = 0$ and $c = -18$

  $\qquad\quad x^2 = 9$ $\qquad$ (Dividing both sides by 2)

  $\qquad\qquad x = 3$ or $x = -3$ In this case, there are two solutions. You could write $x = \pm 3$

  (b) $(x + 5)^2 = 0$

  $\qquad x + 5 = 0$

  $\qquad\qquad x = -5$ $\qquad$ In this case, there is only one solution.

  (c) $\quad x^2 + 1 = 0$ $\qquad$ If x^2 must be positive, there are no solutions to this equation.

  These equations may be represented graphically and this can help in understanding the nature of the solutions.

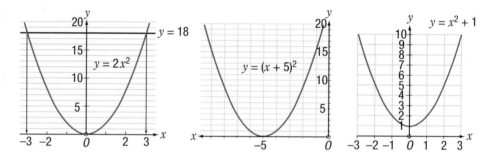

- Some quadratic equations can be solved by factorisation. This uses the fact that if the product of two numbers is zero, then at least one of those numbers must be zero. Here are some examples.

  (a) $\qquad x^2 + 7x = 0$ $\qquad$ The terms have a common factor of x.

  $\qquad x(x + 7) = 0$ $\qquad$ The factorised form shows that x or $x + 7$ must be zero.

  $\qquad x = 0$ or $x = -7$

  (b) $\quad x^2 - 3x - 10 = 0$ $\qquad$ This will factorise using double brackets.

  $\qquad\qquad -5 \times 2 = -10 \quad -5 + 2 = -3$

  $\qquad (x - 5)(x + 2) = 0 \qquad x - 5$ or $x + 2$ must be zero.

  $\qquad x = 5$ or $x = -2$

- Some quadratics cannot be factorised. However, they can be solved by **completing the square**. Here is an example.

  $x^2 + 2x - 7$ cannot be factorised.

▶ *continued*

Completing the square, $x^2 + 2x - 7 = (x + 1)^2 - 1 - 7 = (x + 1)^2 - 8$

To solve $x^2 + 2x - 7 = 0$

rewrite as $(x + 1)^2 - 8 = 0$

$(x + 1)^2 = 8$

$x + 1 = \pm\sqrt{8} = \pm 2.828...$

$\quad\quad x = -1 + 2.828...$ or $x = -1 - 2.828...$

$\quad\quad x = 1.83 \quad\quad$ or $x = -3.83$ to 3 significant figures.

The solution can also be expressed in **surd form**.

$x + 1 = \pm\sqrt{8} = \pm\sqrt{(4 \times 2)} = \pm\sqrt{4} \times \sqrt{2} = \pm 2\sqrt{2}$

$x = -1 \pm 2\sqrt{2}$

- Another application of completing the square is to find the minimum value of a quadratic.

- A different approach to solving a quadratic equation of the form $ax^2 + bx + c = 0$ is to use the formula $x = \dfrac{-b \pm \sqrt{(b^2 - 4ac)}}{2a}$

- Equations with algebraic fractions can lead to quadratic equations.

Definitions

- **Completing the square** writing a quadratic expression in the form $a(x + p)^2 + q$, where a, p and q are integers
- **Surd form** based on surds which are inexact roots of whole numbers, e.g. $2\sqrt{3}$

❶ Examiner's tips

- You may need to rearrange a quadratic equation to put it in an appropriate form before trying to solve it by the methods given in this section.

Worked example

Example 1

Find the minimum value of $x^2 - 4x + 10$ and the value of x where this occurs.

Solution 1

Completing the square gives

$x^2 - 4x + 10 = (x - 2)^2 - 2^2 + 10$

$= (x - 2)^2 + 6$

$(x - 2)^2$ cannot be negative, so its minimum value is 0 when $x = 2$

When $(x - 2)^2 = 0$ $x^2 - 4x + 10 = 0 + 6 = 6$

The minimum value of $x^2 - 4x + 10$ is 6 and this occurs when $x = 2$

Example 2

Use the quadratic formula to solve

$x^2 - 5x - 11 = 0$

Give your solutions correct to 3 significant figures.

Solution 2

$x^2 - 5x - 11 = 0$

The equation is in the usual form with $a = 1$
$b = -5$ and $c = -11$

$x = 5 \pm \sqrt{(-5)^2 - 4 \times 1 \times (-11)} = \dfrac{5 \pm \sqrt{69}}{2}$

$x = 6.653...$ or $x = -1.653...$

$x = 6.65$ or $x = -1.65$ to 3 significant figures.

Example 3

Solve $\dfrac{1}{2x + 3} + \dfrac{1}{x - 1} = 2$

Give your solutions correct to 3 significant figures.

Solution 3

$\dfrac{1}{2x + 3} + \dfrac{1}{x - 1} = 2$

(Multiply both sides by $(2x + 3)$ and $(x - 1)$.

$x - 1 + 2x + 3 = 2(2x + 3)(x - 1)$

$3x + 2 = 2(2x^2 + x - 3)$

$3x + 2 = 4x^2 + 2x - 6$

$4x^2 - x - 8 = 0$

This cannot be factorised.

Use the formula with $a = 4$ $b = -1$ $c = -8$

$x = 1 \pm \sqrt{(-1)^2 - 4 \times 4 \times (-8)} = \dfrac{1 \pm \sqrt{129}}{8}$

$x = 1.5447...$ or $x = -1.2947...$

$x = 1.54$ or $x = -1.29$ to 3 significant figures

Did you know?

- It could be argued that every quadratic equation has two solutions.

$(x - 2)(x - 3) = 0$

$x = 2$ or $x = 3$

$(x - 3)(x - 3) = 0$

$x = 3$ (repeated)

$x^2 + 1 = 0$

There are two solutions but you won't find them on the real number line!

Can you answer these questions?

1. Solve these equations

   (a) $x^2 - 49 = 0$ (b) $x^2 + 8x = 0$ (c) $x^2 - 7x + 10 = 0$

   (d) $x^2 + 5x = 6$

2. Solve these equations. Give your solutions correct to 3 significant figures.

   (a) $2x^2 + 3x - 4 = 0$ (b) $\dfrac{1}{x - 1} + \dfrac{2}{x - 3} = 5$

Look on the CD for more exam practice questions

Simultaneous linear and quadratic equations and loci

Key facts

- Solving **simultaneous equations** where one is **linear** and the other is **quadratic** can be done by substituting information from the linear equation into the quadratic.

- If you have drawn the graphs of two equations on the same axes, then the simultaneous solutions of those equations may be found at the points of intersection of the graphs.

- If you have solved a pair of simultaneous equations, then the values found tell you the coordinates of the points of intersection of their graphs.

- The path followed by a moving point is called the locus of the point as it moves according to some rule. You may need to sketch the locus or give its equation.

- The locus of a point that moves so that its distance from a fixed point O is always r cm is a circle with centre O and radius r cm.

- The equation of a circle with centre at the origin and radius r, is $x^2 + y^2 = r^2$

- You can calculate the points of intersection of a circle with a straight line by finding the solutions of the simultaneous equations representing the circle and the line.

Definitions

- **Simultaneous equations** a set of two or more equations involving the same variables and with the same solutions
- **Linear (equation)** equation (or relationship) which has only x and constant terms giving a straight line graph
- **Quadratic (equation)** can be written in the form $ax^2 + bx + c = 0$ where a, b and c are constants

❶ Examiner's tips

- When solving simultaneous linear and quadratic equations, you may need to rearrange the linear equation first to put it in an appropriate form for substitution into the quadratic.
- When giving answers rounded to a specified degree of accuracy, save any rounding until the last step.

Worked example

Example 1

A point $P(x, y)$ moves so that its distance from the line $x = 1$ is the same as its distance from the line $y = 3$ Sketch the locus of P and find its equation.

Solution 1

The distance of P from the line $x = 1$ is $x - 1$

The distance of P from the line $y = 3$ is $y - 3$

The equation of the locus is $y - 3 = x - 1$ which simplifies to $y = x + 2$

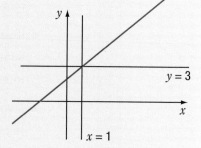

Example 2

Find the coordinates of the points where the circle with equation $x^2 + y^2 = 20$ intersects the line with equation $y = x + 3$

Give your answers correct to 3 significant figures.

Solution 2

$x^2 + (x + 3)^2 = 20$ (Substituting for y in the equation of the circle.)

$x^2 + x^2 + 6x + 9 = 20$ (Expanding the brackets.)

$2x^2 + 6x - 11 = 0$ (Collecting the terms on one side of the equation.)

$x = \dfrac{-6 \pm \sqrt{(36 + 88)}}{4} = \dfrac{-6 \pm \sqrt{124}}{4}$

$x = 1.283...$ or $x = -4.283...$ (Substitute these values in the linear equation to find the y values.)

When $x = 1.28$, $y = 4.28$

When $x = -4.28$, $y = -1.28$

The coordinates of the points of intersection are $(1.28, 4.28)$, $(-4.28, -1.28)$

Did you know?

- The graph of $y = x^2$, for example, is a parabola. A parabola may be defined as the locus of a point that moves so that its distance from a fixed point is the same as its distance from a fixed line.

Can you answer these questions?

1. Solve these pairs of simultaneous equations.

   (a) $x + y = 10$ and $y = 2x^2$

   (b) $2x - y = 8$ and $x^2 + y^2 = 16$

2. Find the equation of the locus of a point that moves so that it is equidistant from the points $(3, 0)$ and $(0, -3)$.

Look on the CD for more exam practice questions

Key facts

- Two shapes are similar if corresponding angles are equal and pairs of corresponding sides are in the same ratio.

- If two shapes are similar each is an enlargement of the other. For example, these rectangles are similar because all angles are equal to 90° and corresponding sides are in the same ratio.

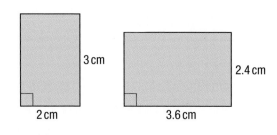

Lengths 3 cm : 3.6 cm = 1 : 1.2   Widths 2 cm : 2.4 cm = 1 : 1.2

The larger rectangle is an enlargement of the smaller with scale factor 1.2

- As with proving that triangles are congruent, it is not necessary to compare all sides and all angles to show that shapes are similar. Triangles are similar if they satisfy one of these conditions:

(a)   **(b)**

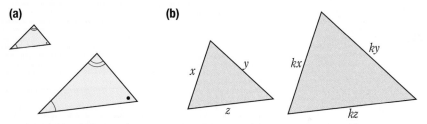

(a) Corresponding angles are equal (triangles are equiangular).

In practice it is sufficient to find two pairs of equal angles, as the third pair must then be equal.

(b) Corresponding sides are in the same ratio.

- Ratio calculations are used to find unknown quantities.

- If two shapes are similar with sides in the ratio $1 : n$ the ratio of the areas is $1 : n^2$ For example,

Ratio of sides = 2 : 6 = 1 : 3

Area A = 4 cm^2 Area B = 36cm^2

Ratio of areas = 4 : 36 = 1 : 9 = 1 : 3^2

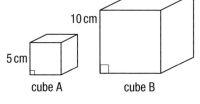

square A   square B

- If two shapes are similar with sides in the ratio $1 : n$ the ratio of the volumes is $1 : n^3$ For example,

Ratio of sides = 5 : 10 = 1 : 2

Volume A = 5 × 5 × 5 = 125 cm^3

Volume B = 10 × 10 × 10 = 1000 cm^3

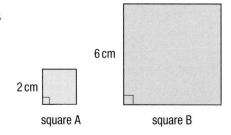

cube A   cube B

Ratio of volumes = 125 : 1000 = 1 : 8 = 1 : 2^3

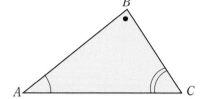
Worked example

Example 1

These six-sided shapes are similar. Find the lengths x, y, and z.

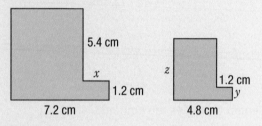

Solution 1

Ratio of base lengths $= 7.2 : 4.8 = 72 : 48 = 6 : 4$

$= 3 : 2$

$\dfrac{x}{1.2} = 3 : 2$

$x = \dfrac{3}{2} \times 1.2 = 1.8\,\text{cm}$

$\dfrac{y}{1.2} = \dfrac{2}{3}$

$y = \dfrac{2}{3} \times 1.2 = 0.8\,\text{cm}$

Height of larger shape $= 1.2 + 5.4 = 6.6\,\text{cm}$

$\dfrac{z}{6.6} = \dfrac{2}{3}$

$z = \dfrac{2}{3} \times 6.6 = 4.4\,\text{cm}$

Example 2

(a) Prove that triangles *ABC* and *ADE* are similar.

(b) Find x.

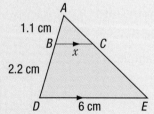

Solution 2

(a) angle *ABC* = angle *ADE* (corresponding angles)

angle *ACB* = angle *AED* (corresponding angles)

angle *D* is common

triangles *ABC* and *ADE* are equiangular

(corresponding angles are equal)

(b) $\dfrac{AB}{AD} = \dfrac{BC}{DE} = \dfrac{AC}{AE}$

$\dfrac{1.1}{3.3} = \dfrac{x}{6}$ (Using first two ratios.)

$x = \dfrac{1}{3} \times 6 = 2\,\text{cm}$

Example 3

A car maker produces 2 similar cars whose lengths are in the ratio of 5 : 6. Find

(a) the width of the larger car if the smaller car is 130 cm wide.

(b) the windscreen area of the larger car if that of smaller car is 600 cm^2

(c) the engine capacity of the smaller car if that of the larger car is 1728 cc

Solution 3

(a) Ratio of lengths $= 5 : 6 = 1 : 1.2$ $(6 \div 5)$

Width of larger car $= 1.2 \times 130\,\text{cm} = 156\,\text{cm}$

(b) Ratio of areas $= 5^2 : 6^2 = 25 : 36 = 1 : 1.44$

$(36 \div 25$ by calculator)

Windscreen area of larger car $= 1.44 \times 600 =$

$864\,\text{cm}^2$

▶ continued

(c) Ratio of volumes = $5^3 : 6^3 = 1 : 1.728$

(capacity is volume, $6^3 \div 5^3 = 1.728$)

Capacity of smaller car = $1728 \div 1.728$

= 1000 cc

or

ratio of volumes = $5^3 : 6^3 = 0.578 : 1$

(capacity is volume)

capacity of smaller car = $0.578 \times 1728 = 1000$cc

(Use the stored calculator value of $\dfrac{5^3}{6^3}$ as 0.578

is only correct to 3 sf)

Can you answer these questions?

1. Are these true or false?

   (a) All squares are similar to each other.

   (b) All isosceles triangles are similar to each other.

   (c) All equilateral triangles are similar to each other.

2. Two triangles are similar and the sides of one are 6 cm, 7 cm and 8 cm. If the shortest side of the other is 15 cm, find the lengths of the other 2 sides.

3. Triangle ABC is right-angled at B and BD is perpendicular to AC.

   Prove that triangles ABC, ABD and BDC are all similar to each other.

4. A model of a church has a base area that is $\dfrac{1}{100}$ the ground area of the church.

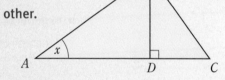

   (a) What scale is used?

   (b) If the length of the model is 4 m, what is the length of the church?

   (c) If the volume of the church spire is 3000 m^3, find the volume of the spire on the model.

5. The length of a yacht is 10 m and the length of its model is 20 cm.

   (a) What scale is used?

   (b) Find the height of the mast of the model if the yacht's mast is 14 m high.

   (c) Find the sail area of the yacht if the model's sails have an area of 180 cm^2.

   (d) The volume of the yacht's hull is 150 m^3. Find the volume of the hull on the model.

Look on the CD for more exam practice questions

Did you know?

● All A format (A1   A2   A3   A4) sheets of paper are similar, and each increase in size doubles the area, for example A3 is double the area of A4

Key facts

- If y is directly proportional to x then this may be written as $y \propto x$ and it follows that $y = kx$ for some constant value k known as the constant of proportionality. In this case, the graph of y against x is a straight line passing through the origin, with gradient k. Here is an example.

x	5	10	15	20
y	15	30		60

The table shows values of x and y where $y \propto x$. In this case, $y = 3x$ and so the constant of proportionality is 3
The missing value must be $3 \times 15 = 45$

- Direct proportion is not restricted to **linear relationships**. It may be, for example, that y is directly proportional to the square of x, written as $y \propto x^2$, and so $y = kx^2$. In general, if $y \propto x^n$ then $y = kx^n$.

- If y is inversely proportional to x then y is directly proportional to the **reciprocal** of x. This is written as $y \propto \dfrac{1}{x}$ and it follows that $y = \dfrac{k}{x}$ where k is the constant of proportionality.

- In general, if y is inversely proportional to x^n then $y = \dfrac{k}{x^n}$ where k is the constant of proportionality.

Worked example

Example 1

Given that $y \propto x^2$ and that $y = 4.5$ when $x = 3$
find y when $x = 5$

Solution 1

$y = kx^2$

$4.5 = k \times 3^2 = 9k$ (Substitute the known values.)

$k = \dfrac{4.5}{9} = 0.5$ (Rearrange to find k.)

$y = 0.5x^2$ (Find the formula relating y and x.)

When $x = 5$ $y = 0.5 \times 5^2 = 12.5$

Example 2

Given that $y \propto \sqrt{x}$ and that $y = 12$ when $x = 9$
find y when $x = 25$

Solution 2

$y = k\sqrt{x}$

$12 = k \times \sqrt{9} = 3k$ (Substitute the known values.)

$k = 4$ (Rearrange to find k.)

$y = 4\sqrt{x}$ (Find the formula relating y and x.)

When $x = 25$ $y = 4 \times \sqrt{25} = 4 \times 5 = 20$

▶ continued

Example 3

y is inversely proportional to x. Given that $y = 5$ when $x = 2$ find y when $x = 4$

Solution 3

$y = \dfrac{k}{x}$

$5 = \dfrac{k}{2}$ (Substitute the known values.)

$k = 10$ (Rearrange to find k.)

$y = \dfrac{10}{x}$ (Find the formula relating y and x.)

When $x = 4$ $y = \dfrac{10}{4} = 2.5$

Example 4

y is inversely proportional to $\sqrt{x}$ and $y = 6$ when $x = 4$ Find y when $x = 25$

Solution 4

$y = \dfrac{k}{\sqrt{x}}$

$6 = \dfrac{k}{\sqrt{4}} = \dfrac{k}{2}$

$k = 12$

$y = \dfrac{12}{\sqrt{x}}$

When $x = 25$ $y = \dfrac{12}{\sqrt{25}} = \dfrac{12}{5} = 2.4$

Definitions

- **Linear relationships** relationships having no terms with index numbers and giving a straight line graph
- **Reciprocal** 1 divided by a number: e.g. reciprocal of $2 = \dfrac{1}{2}$

❶ Examiner's tips

- To get started with a problem on proportion, write any given statement about the proportion in symbols and introduce a constant of proportionality. This will give you a formula relating the two variables.

Can you answer these questions?

1. y is directly proportional to x^3 and $y = 13.5$ when $x = 3$
   Find y when $x = 4$
2. y is inversely proportional to x^2 and $y = 4$ when $x = 5$
   Find y when $x = 20$

Did you know?

- The area of a circle is directly proportional to the square of its radius. This may be written as $A \propto r^2$ leading to $A = kr^2$. In this case, the constant of proportionality, k, is the special number π.

Look on the CD for more exam practice questions

Key facts

- A vector quantity has both size (**magnitude**), and direction.

- Displacement is distance in a specified direction so displacement is a vector, whereas distance alone is not. The displacement from A to B is written as $\overrightarrow{AB}$

- A single letter may be used to represent a vector, shown in bold print to distinguish it from a distance. The diagram shows the vector **a** as a line on a grid. The magnitude of the vector is determined by its length and its direction is shown by the arrow.

  The vector **a** may be described as a column vector in the same way as a **translation**.

  $$\mathbf{a} = \begin{pmatrix} 3 \\ 2 \end{pmatrix}$$

- The magnitude of the vector $\begin{pmatrix} x \\ y \end{pmatrix}$ is $\sqrt{x^2 + y^2}$

- Two vectors are equal if they have the same magnitude and the same direction.

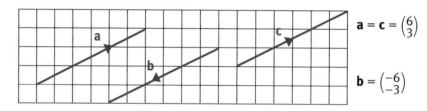

$$\mathbf{a} = \mathbf{c} = \begin{pmatrix} 6 \\ 3 \end{pmatrix}$$

$$\mathbf{b} = \begin{pmatrix} -6 \\ -3 \end{pmatrix}$$

In the diagram $\mathbf{a} = \mathbf{c} = -\mathbf{b}$ **b** has the same magnitude as **a** and **c** but the opposite direction.

- For any non-zero number k, $k\mathbf{p}$ is a vector parallel to the vector **p**.
  If $\mathbf{p} = \begin{pmatrix} a \\ b \end{pmatrix}$ then $k\mathbf{p} = k = \begin{pmatrix} a \\ b \end{pmatrix} = \begin{pmatrix} ka \\ kb \end{pmatrix}$

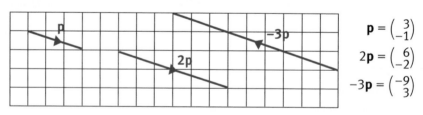

$$\mathbf{p} = \begin{pmatrix} 3 \\ -1 \end{pmatrix}$$

$$2\mathbf{p} = \begin{pmatrix} 6 \\ -2 \end{pmatrix}$$

$$-3\mathbf{p} = \begin{pmatrix} -9 \\ 3 \end{pmatrix}$$

2**p** is twice as long as **p** and in the same direction. −3**p** is three times as long as **p** and in the opposite direction.

▶ *continued*

- Vectors may be added as shown in the diagram.

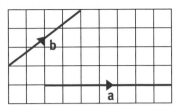 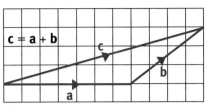

In column vectors, $\mathbf{a} = \begin{pmatrix} 7 \\ 0 \end{pmatrix}$ $\mathbf{b} = \begin{pmatrix} 4 \\ 3 \end{pmatrix}$ $\mathbf{c} = \begin{pmatrix} 7 \\ 0 \end{pmatrix} + \begin{pmatrix} 4 \\ 3 \end{pmatrix} = \begin{pmatrix} 11 \\ 3 \end{pmatrix}$

- $\mathbf{a} - \mathbf{b}$ is the same as $\mathbf{a} + -\mathbf{b}$

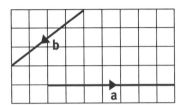 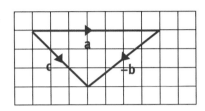

In column vectors, $\mathbf{c} = \begin{pmatrix} 7 \\ 0 \end{pmatrix} + \begin{pmatrix} -4 \\ -3 \end{pmatrix} = \begin{pmatrix} 7 \\ 0 \end{pmatrix} - \begin{pmatrix} 4 \\ 3 \end{pmatrix} = \begin{pmatrix} 3 \\ -3 \end{pmatrix}$

- When an origin O is defined, the position vector of a point is the vector from the origin to that point. If the coordinates of the point are (a, b) then the position vector is $\begin{pmatrix} a \\ b \end{pmatrix}$

Definitions

- **Magnitude** size
- **Translation** a slide with all points in a shape having the same displacement

Worked example

Find the magnitude of the vector
$\vec{AB} = \begin{pmatrix} 4 \\ -3 \end{pmatrix}$

Solution

$AB = \sqrt{4^2 + (-3)^2}$

$\quad = \sqrt{16 + 9}$

$\quad = 5$

❶ Examiner's tips

- You can't write in bold to show a vector, so write $\underline{a}$ to represent **a**.

Can you answer these questions?

1. Draw a diagram to show that a + b = b + a
2. A is the point (4, 7) and B is the point (−2, 11). Find $\vec{AB}$ as a column vector.

Did you know?

- Vectors can be used in 3-D and even higher dimensions.

Look on the CD for more exam practice questions

Key facts

- A **function** is a rule that changes a number. It is often denoted by one of the letters f, g or h but any letter may be used.

- Read f(x) as 'f of x'. If, for example, f(x) = $2x + 3$ then the function f will change a number by multiplying it by 2 and then adding 3.
  In this case, f(4) = $2 \times 4 + 3 = 11$ and f(−5) = $2 \times -5 + 3 = -7$

- The graph of y = f(x) + a is the same shape as the graph of y = f(x) but is moved a distance of a units parallel to the x-axis. If $a > 0$ then the movement (a **translation**) is up and if $a < 0$ then the movement is down. The movement may be described by the translation vector $\binom{0}{a}$ Here is an example.

  The diagram shows the graphs of $y = x^2$, $y = x^2 + 2$ and $y = x^2 - 3$

  The graph of $y = x^2$ is given a translation of $\binom{0}{2}$ to make the graph of $y = x^2 + 2$ and a translation of $\binom{0}{-3}$ to make the graph of $y = x^2 - 3$

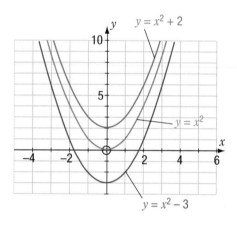

- The graph of y = f($x + a$) is the same shape as the graph of y = f(x) but is moved a distance of a units parallel to the y-axis. If $a > 0$ then the translation is to the left and if $a < 0$ then the translation is to the right. The movement may be described by the translation vector $\binom{-a}{0}$ Here is an example.

  The diagram shows the graphs of y = f(x), y = f($x - 4$) and y = f($x + 3$) for some function f(x).

- Transformations may be combined. For example, the graph of y = f($x + 2$) − 3 may be obtained as a translation of the graph of y = f(x) by 2 units to the left and 3 units down. The translation may be represented by the translation vector $\binom{-2}{-3}$

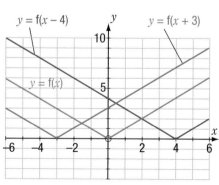

▶ *continued*

- The graph of $y = -f(x)$ is the **reflection** of the graph of $y = f(x)$ in the x-axis.

- The graph of $y = f(-x)$ is the reflection of the graph of $y = f(x)$ in the y-axis.

- The graph of $y = af(x)$ is a stretch of the graph of $y = f(x)$ with **scale factor** a parallel to the y-axis.

- The graph of $y = f(ax)$ is a stretch of the graph of $y = f(x)$ with scale factor $\frac{1}{a}$ parallel to the x-axis.

Definitions

- **Translation** a slide with all points in a shape having the same displacement
- **Reflection** transformation where image is same as object but reversed orientation
- **Scale factor** factor by which shape or function is enlarged

❶ Examiner's tips

- You can use tracing paper to make a copy of a graph and transform it with a translation or reflection.

Worked example

$g(x) = x^2$

(a) Find the value of   (i) $g(5)$ (ii) $g(-6)$

(b) Find an expression for   (i) $g(x + 1)$ (ii) $g(x) + 1$

Solution

(a) (i) $g(5) = 5^2 = 25$ (ii) $g(-6) = (-6)^2 = 36$

(b) (i) $g(x + 1) = (x + 1)^2$ (ii) $g(x) + 1 = x^2 + 1$

Did you know?

- The sine curve repeats itself every $360°$, so sin $(x + 360°) = \sin x$ for any value of x. This is an example of a periodic function.

Can you answer these questions?

1. $f(x) = x^3 - 1$

    Find an expression for   (a) $2f(x) + 3$ (b) $f(2x) + 3$

2. Describe the transformation that would map the graph of $y = f(x)$ onto the graph of $y = f(x - 3) - 5$

3. The graph of $y = x^2$ is stretched by a factor of 3 parallel to the x-axis. What is the equation of the new graph?

Look on the CD for more exam practice questions

Essential formulae

Compound measures

- average speed $(S) = \dfrac{\text{total distance travelled } (D)}{\text{total time taken } (T)}$

$$S = \frac{D}{T} \qquad D = S \times T \qquad T = \frac{D}{S}$$

- density $(D) = \dfrac{\text{mass } (M)}{\text{volume } (V)}$

$$M = D \times V \qquad D = \frac{M}{V} \qquad V = \frac{M}{D}$$

Perimeter and area of 2-D shapes

- Perimeter of a rectangle = 2 (length + width)

- Area of a rectangle = length × width

- Circumference of a circle = πd

- Area of a circle = πr^2

- Area of a triangle = $\frac{1}{2}$ base × height

Volume and surface area of 3-D shapes

- Volume of a cuboid = length × width × height

- Volume of a cylinder = $\pi r^2 h$

- Surface area of a sphere = $4\pi r^2$

- Total surface area of a cylinder = $2\pi rh + \pi r^2$

- Total surface area of a solid cone = $\pi rl + \pi r^2$

- $1 \text{ cm}^3 = 1000 \text{ mm}^3 \quad 1 \text{ m}^3 = 1\,000\,000 \text{ cm}^3$

To measure:	Length	Mass	Capacity
Converting between imperial units	1 mile = 1760 yards 1 yard = 3 feet (ft) 1 foot = 12 inches (in)	1 ton = 20 hundredweight (cwt) 1 cwt = 112 pounds (lb) 1 lb = 16 ounces (oz) 1 stone = 14 lb	1 gallon = 8 pints 1 pint = 20 fluid ounces (fl oz)
Converting between metric units	1 m = 100 cm = 1000 mm 1 km = 1000 m 1 cm = 1000 mm	1 g = 1000 mg 1 kg = 1000 g 1 t = 1000 kg	1 l = 100 cl = 1000 ml 1 kl = 1000 l 1 cl = 10 ml

Answers

1 Number (page 8)

1. (a) 8 10 12 14 16
   (b) 9 11 13 15
   (c) 11 13 (d) 9 16 (e) 9 12 15
   (f) 10 12 15
2. (a) $2 \times 5 \times 7^2$ (b) 2×5^3
   (c) $2 \times 2 \times 7$
3. (a) 529 (b) 13 924 (c) 12 (d) 96
   (e) 1296 (f) 5.832 (g) 21.4375 (h) 9
4. (a) −147 (b) 227 (c) −465 (d) 0
   (e) −11 (f) 138 (g) −1628
5. (a) $\frac{1}{10}$ (b) 25 (c) $\frac{7}{41}$ (d) $\frac{20}{23}$ (e) $\frac{1}{12}$

2 Angles (page 11)

1. (a) $a = 28°$ (b) $b = 50°$ $c = 55°$ $d = 50°$
2. (a) $x = 27°$ (b) $y = 140°$ $(x = 20°)$
3. 45° 45° 90°
4. $x = 36°$ $(10x = 360°)$
5. exterior angle = 40° interior angle = 140°

3 Scatter graphs (page 13)

1. (a) positive correlation
   (b) zero correlation (c) negative correlation
2. (a)

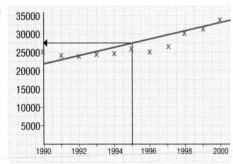

From the scatter graph, the estimated number of finishers in 1995 was 28 000.
   (b) The proposal to extend the line of best fit to estimate the number of finishers in 2020 is not a good idea since the method gives unreliable results outside the limits of the plotted points.

4 Fractions (page 15)

1. (a) $\frac{1}{2} = \frac{2}{4}$ (b) $\frac{3}{5} = \frac{6}{10}$ (c) $\frac{3}{8} = \frac{15}{40}$
   (d) $\frac{4}{6} = \frac{2}{3}$ (e) $\frac{25}{50} = \frac{1}{2}$ (f) $\frac{3}{4} = \frac{12}{16}$
   (g) $\frac{15}{81} = \frac{15}{27}$ (h) $\frac{11}{33} = \frac{1}{3}$ (i) $\frac{95}{5} = \frac{19}{1}$
2. (a) $\frac{4}{5}$ (b) $\frac{7}{9}$ (c) $\frac{1}{5}$ (d) $\frac{13}{14}$
3. (a) $\frac{79}{8}$ (b) $\frac{136}{3}$ (c) $\frac{25}{2}$ (d) $\frac{74}{5}$
4. (a) $7\frac{11}{12}$ (b) $15\frac{2}{3}$ (c) $1\frac{7}{11}$ (d) $12\frac{11}{12}$

5. (a) $1\frac{9}{28}$ (b) $\frac{2}{5}$ (c) $\frac{37}{48}$ (d) $1\frac{1}{6}$
   (e) $10\frac{19}{20}$ (f) $3\frac{3}{4}$ (g) 1 (h) $9\frac{5}{24}$ (i) $6\frac{3}{20}$
6. (a) $\frac{2}{9}$ (b) $\frac{3}{16}$ (c) $\frac{23}{30}$ (d) $1\frac{11}{14}$ (e) $\frac{7}{15}$ (f) $8\frac{13}{16}$
7. (a) $1\frac{1}{4}$ (b) 16 (c) $1\frac{9}{10}$ (d) 38 (e) $5\frac{5}{6}$ (f) $5\frac{199}{220}$
8. (a) 3 (b) $\frac{67}{120}$ (c) 21 (d) $\frac{1}{100}$ (e) $7\frac{1}{26}$
   (f) $73\frac{2}{3}$ (g) $55\frac{1}{4}$ (h) 64
9. (a) She can make 57 scraps altogether.
   (b) She sold $9\frac{11}{12}$ melons altogether.

5 Expressions and sequences (page 18)

1. (a) $2x + 2y$ (b) $mn\,(3m + 2n + 5)$
2. $\frac{1}{ab}$
3. (a) 17 (b) −2
4. $8s + 6b$
5. (a) $6x^5$ (b) $3ab^{-2}$ (c) $1000m^{-3}n^9$
6. (a) 1 (b) $\frac{1}{27}$ (c) 4
7. 30, 41, 54
8. 2, 7, 12
9. nth term = $7n + 3$

6 Measure (page 20)

1. (a) $240\,\text{cm} \div 80 = 3\,\text{cm}$
      The door will be 3 cm high in the model.
   (b) $18.75\,\text{cm} \times 80 = 1500\,\text{cm}$
      The height of the building is 1500 cm or 15 m in real life.
2. You need to draw a rectangle of 16 cm × 6 cm, and label it 1 : 300
3. First, convert the distances to the same units.
   8 km = 800 000 cm
   16 : 800 000 = 1 : 50 000
4. Use the formula $S = \dfrac{D}{T}$
   (a) $42 \div 6.5625 = 6.4$
      Brett's average speed was 6.4 km/h.
   (b) $42 \div 6 = 7$
      Siobhan's average speed was 7 km/h.
   (c) $\dfrac{20\text{ minutes}}{60\text{ minutes}} = \dfrac{1}{3}$ $42 \div 8\frac{1}{3} = 42 \div \dfrac{25}{3}$
      $= 42 \times \dfrac{3}{25} = \dfrac{126}{25}$
      Lance's average speed was $5\frac{1}{25}$ km/h or 5.04 km/h
5. (a) Use the formula $T = \dfrac{D}{S}$
      $(220 \div 85) \times 60 = \dfrac{220}{85} \times 60$
      $= \dfrac{44}{17} \times 60$
      = 155 minutes
      = 2 hours and 35 minutes

(b) 100 km at 95 km/h

$T = 100/95$

$= 1\frac{5}{95}$

$= 1\frac{1}{19}$ hours

120 at 85 km/h

$T = 120/85$

$= 1\frac{35}{85}$

$= 1\frac{7}{17}$ hours

$1\frac{1}{19} + 1\frac{7}{17} = 2\frac{17 + 133}{323}$

The LCD of 19 and 17 is 323

$= 2\frac{150}{323}$

$= 2\frac{1}{2}$ hours

He would have saved 5 minutes.

6 (a) 1.19 cm³   (b) 2394 g   (c) 22.9 cm³

(d) silver

7 (a) area, because the expression has dimensions (length × length)

(b) none, because the first term in the expression has the dimensions (length × length) and the second term has only the dimension (length)

(c) volume, because the expression has dimensions (length × length × length)

(d) length, because the expression has the dimension (length)

8 (a) 24 km   (b) 11.4 kg   (c) 81 litres

(d) 36.3 cm

9 (a) 44 pounds   (b) 28.4 gallons

(c) 280 miles   (d) 2.6 feet

7 Decimals and fractions (page 22)

1 (a) 0.02   0.2   0.225   0.251   2.001

(b) 7.008   7.0099   7.089   7.098   7.2

2 (a) 11.3   (b) 7.24   (c) 229.15   (d) 451.27

(e) 6.16   (f) 24.82   (g) 9.22   (h) 2.9169

3 (a) 32.8   (b) 2483.99   (c) 21.4   (d) 200

(e) 10.58   (f) 1.044   (g) 6.65   (h) 0.0068

4 (a) 4.995   (b) 0.000778   (c) 0.0010118

(d) 0.0004   (e) 30   (f) 125   (g) 37

(h) 0.001085

5 (a) 1092 (b) 1092   (c) 0.1092   (d) 10.92

6 (a) 0.48 (b) 4.8   (c) 0.48   (d) 0.48

7 (a) $\frac{31}{40}$ (b) $3\frac{17}{20}$ (c) $1\frac{5}{8}$ (d) $25\frac{1}{4}$

8 (a) 0.8   (b) 0.875   (c) 0.8333... (d) 0.58333...

9 (a) $8\frac{9}{11}$ (b) $\frac{7}{11}$ (c) $4\frac{5}{6}$ (d) $\frac{12}{13}$

10 (a) 50   (b) 2.1   (c) 0.014   (d) 670

8 Expanding brackets and factorising (page 24)

1   $9947^2 - 53^2 = (9947 + 53)(9947 - 53)$

$= 10\,000 \times 9894 = 98\,940\,000$

2 (a) $8x - 12$ (b) $12x^2 + 3xy$

(c) $x^2 - x - 6$ (d) $6x^2 + 8x - 30$ (e) $9x^2 - 6x + 1$

3 (a) $5x(x - 2)$ (b) $4x^2y^3(3 + 2y - x)$

(c) $(x - 3)(x - 5)$ (d) $(3x + 4y^2)(3x - 4y^2)$

9 2-D Shapes (page 27)

1 (a) True   (b) True

2 (a) 4 tins   (b) 20.2 m

3 As a trapezium: $A = \frac{1}{2}(9 + 15) \times 4 = 48$ cm²

As large triangle – small triangle:

$A = \frac{1}{2} \times 15 \times 10 - \frac{1}{2} \times 9 \times 6 = 48$ cm²

4 31.8 cm   5 295 cm²   6 57.1 cm²

10 Linear Equations (page 29)

1 $a = 5$ 2 $c = 4\frac{1}{2}$ 3 $x = 64$ 4 $y = -2$ 5 $p = 9$

6 $n = 13$ 7 $h = 17$ 8 $x = -3$

9 $m = 1\frac{1}{2}$ 10 $w = \frac{2}{5}$ 11 $k = \frac{1}{6}$ 12 $q = 8$

13 (a) $a = 5$ $b = \frac{1}{4}$ (b) $x = 3$ $y = 7$

(c) $p = 2$ $q = -4$

11 Collecting and recording data (page 30)

1 (a) qualitative   (b) quantitative

(c) quantitative   (d) qualitative

2 (a) continuous   (b) continuous   (c) discrete

3 (a)

Outcome	Tally	Frequency
1	||	2
2	|||	3
3	||||	4
4	||||	4
5	|||	3
6	||||	4

(b)

Result	Sally	David
1	2	2
2	3	1
3	4	3
4	4	3
5	3	5
6	4	6

4 (a)

Age range (years)	Tally	Frequency
0–7	||||	4
8–18	JHT ||	7
19–25	|	1
26–40	||	2
41–55	|||	3
56 and over	JHT JHT |	11

(b) The modal class interval was 66 and over.

5 (a) This question is biased because the form 'Do you agree…' suggests that the respondent should answer 'yes'. A better question would be: Which of the following media do you consider a good source of information?

Television   Radio   Newspapers   Magazines

☐   ☐   ☐   ☐

Other (please specify) _____

None of these ☐

(b) The question is problematic because the data is continuous. Some people may spend no time listening to the radio each day; others may spend less than an hour. There are also different time frames that the researcher needs to specify: firstly, how often do people listen to their radios (how many times per week or month), and secondly, for how long do they listen to it (how many hours at a time)? You can design your improved question for either of these pieces of information, for example,

Approximately how many hours per week do you spend listening to the radio?

0–5 hours   5–10 hours   10–20 hours

☐   ☐   ☐

20–30 hours   More than 30 hours

☐   ☐

(c) This question is problematic, because there may be other radio programs that people prefer. Your 'improved list' should include more items (e.g. competitions, phone-in chat shows, religious programmes, and so on) as well as a space for respondents to specify their own answers.

6 (a) The survey will be biased because the people that are at the cinema on a Saturday evening are probably the people that are already satisfied with the cinema facilities available.

(b) He could choose a more random sample of the population. For example a sample of people of different ages from different areas in his town.

7 (a) A random sample is a sample in which each person has an equal chance of being chosen. For a random sample for this study, you could select a set number of pupils from each class.

(b) For a stratified sample, you could select a particular number of names from each class list.

12 Percentages (page 33)

1 (a) $\frac{1}{5}$ (b) $\frac{22}{25}$ (c) $\frac{9}{40}$ (d) $\frac{1}{10}$ (e) $1\frac{1}{2}$

2 (a) 0.195   (b) 0.28   (c) 0.5   (d) 0.995   (e) 1.0

3 (a) 40   (b) 495   (c) 5.5   (d) 22   (e) £3.42

     (f) 22.75 g   (g) 594 kg   (h) £86.40

4 (a) 1200 − 804 = 396

     396 women attend the conference.

     (b) $\frac{804}{1200} \times \frac{100}{1} = 67\%$

     67% of the delegates are men.

     (c) 30% of 1200 = 0.3 × 1200 = 360

     There are 360 government representatives.

5 Selling price = cost + profit

   = £195 000 + (2.85 × £195 000)

   = £195 000 + £555 750

   = £750 750

6 $\frac{25}{30} \times \frac{100}{1} = 83\%$

7 (a) 8 × £4.95 = £39.60

     £39.60 is greater than her cost price (£18.00), so she made a profit.

     (b) Profit = £39.60 − £18.00 = £21.60

     She made a profit of £21.60

     Percentage profit = (£21.60 ÷ £18.00) × 100

     = 120%

8 100% + 3% = 103%

   103% = 1.03

   £650.00 × (1.03)⁴ = £731.58

   Total interest = £731.58 − £650.00 = £81.58

13 Graphs – including trial and improvement (page 38)

1 (a) (i) 80 shekels   (ii) £ 7   (b) £1 = 8 shekels

2 1 hour 25 minutes

3 (b) $x = 2$ $y = 2$

4 (a) $y = 2x + 1$ (b) $y = -\frac{1}{2}x$

5 (a) (i) $x = 0$ (ii) $x = -1$ 6   (b) $y = x - 8$ (c) $x = 2$ 4

6 $x = 1.24$

14 Transformations (page 40)

1 (a) rotation or enlargement

(b) translation, reflection or rotation

(c) translation   (d) all transformations

(e) enlargement   (f) no transformations

(g) reflection   (h) rotation   (i) enlargement

2 (a) $\begin{pmatrix} 5 \\ 3 \end{pmatrix}$ (b) $\begin{pmatrix} -17 \\ 8 \end{pmatrix}$ (c) $\begin{pmatrix} -12 \\ -12 \end{pmatrix}$

3

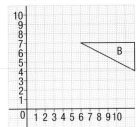

4 (a) translation as described by the vector $\begin{pmatrix} 5 \\ 0 \end{pmatrix}$

(b) reflection through the mirror line $x = 11$

(c) rotation clockwise through 90 degrees about the point (2, 5) and translation down one unit (as described by the vector $\begin{pmatrix} 0 \\ -1 \end{pmatrix}$)

(d) reflection through the mirror line $x = 10.5$ and translation 4 units down (as described by the vector $\begin{pmatrix} 0 \\ -4 \end{pmatrix}$).

5

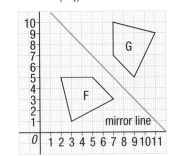

6 Length = 15 m × 3.5 = 52.5 m
   Width = 6 m × 3.5 = 21 m

7 (a) 2   (b) 3   (c) $\frac{1}{6}$

8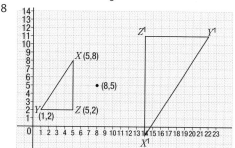

15 Inequalities (page 43)

1 $x = -2$

2 (a) $x < 3$ (b) $x > 5$ (c) $x \geqslant x - 1$ (d) $x < 0$

3 (a) A: $x = -2$ B: $y = x$

   (b) gradient $= -\frac{1}{2}$, $y = -\frac{1}{2}x + 3$

   (c) $y \geqslant x$, $y \leqslant -\frac{1}{2}x + 3$

4 (a) (b)

16 Estimating and accuracy (page 44)

1 (a) 1750   (b) 19.9   (c) 0.489   (d) 7.00
   (e) 1.04

2 (a) 200   (b) 2   (c) 10   (d) 30   (e) 9

3 (a) 590   (b) 0.38   (c) 1.4   (d) 180   (e) 4600

4 (a) $3.8 \times 2.7 \approx 4 \times 3 \approx 12$
   (b) $11.9 \times 2.1 \approx 10 \times 2 \approx 20$
   (c) $0.522 \times 3.14 \approx 0.5 \times 3 \approx 1.5$
   (d) $9.15 \times 0.6 \approx 9 \times 0.6 \approx 5.4$
   (e) $764 \times 2.9 \approx 800 \times 3 \approx 2400$

5 (a) $178 \div 4.5 \approx 200 \div 5 \approx 40$
   (b) $995 \div 120 \approx 1000 \div 100 \approx 10$
   (c) $476 \div 23 \approx 500 \div 20 \approx 25$
   (d) $723 \div 14.8 \approx 700 \div 10 \approx 70$
   (e) $11.7 \div 1.6 \approx 10 \div 2 \approx 5$

6 (a) 6.71   (b) 17.97   (c) 0.5   (d) 1.98   (e) 0.96

7 (a) smallest possible mass = 433.5 g
       greatest possible mass = 434.4 g
   (b) smallest possible mass = 4.5 g
       greatest possible mass = 5.4 g

8 (a) longest possible diameter: 45.4 cm
       shortest possible diameter: 44.5 cm

9 (a) lower bound: 5.85; upper bound: 5.94
   (b) lower bound: 7.825; upper bound: 7.834

   (c) lower bound: 0.3165; upper bound: 0.3174
   (d) lower bound: 46.5; upper bound: 47.4
   (e) lower bound: 5445; upper bound: 5454
   (f) lower bound: 18.45; upper bound: 18.74

10 (a) She has rounded her age to the nearest six
       months.
   (b) lower bound: 9 years 3 months; upper bound:
       9 years 8 months

17 Averages and spread (page 48)

1 $8 \times 10 - 7 \times 11 = 3$

2 97, 124.5, 146.25

18 Formulae (page 50)

1 42   2 $C = lm + pn$

3 $A = 2(ab + bc + ac)$

4 (a) $b = \dfrac{d - ac}{b}$ (b) $r = \sqrt{\left(\dfrac{3V}{\pi h}\right)}$ (c) $m = \dfrac{y - c}{x}$

5 (a) false $A = 2b + C$ is a formula (b) true

19 Pythagoras' theorem (page 52)

1 4.97 cm   2 20 cm

3 (a) 6.24 cm   (b) 4.53 cm   (c) 14.4 cm

4 No, not Pythagorean triple   5 17.7 km

6 3.67 m   7 7.07 cm

20 Trigonometry (page 55)

1 (a) 13.6 cm   (b) 38.6°   (c) 12.1 cm

2 122°

3 length = 2.12 m; angle with ground = 70.5°

4 (a) +   (b) −   (c) −

5 7.58 cm

6 (a) 34.0°   (b) 39.2 cm²

21 Ratio and proportion (page 57)

1 Danielle £2450   Kelly £1750

2 80 km

3 4 glasses

22 Processing, representing and interpreting data (page 58)

1 (a)

Test mark	Frequency
31–40	1
41–50	1
51–60	4
61–70	4
71–80	6
81–90	3
91–100	1

2 (a)

(b) Emails received – lower quartile is approximately 16 and upper quartile is approximately 31

Emails sent – lower quartile is approximately 22 and upper quartile is approximately 48

3 (a) minimum value = 2

maximum value = 25

lower quartile = 3.5

upper quartile = 7.5

(b) This is incorrect. The median shown on the plot is 5 cups. This only shows that out of the 120 people questioned, most respondents drank 5 cups per day – not more than that. In any case, this is a very small sample, and therefore it is impossible to draw broad conclusions about 'most people's' coffee consumption.

4

Age (x years)	Frequency
$10 < x \leqslant 15$	5
$15 < x \leqslant 20$	15
$20 < x \leqslant 25$	45
$25 < x \leqslant 30$	55
$30 < x \leqslant 45$	60
$45 < x \leqslant 55$	30
$55 < x \leqslant 70$	15

23 3-D shapes (page 61)

1 or or

2 (a) circle   (b) triangle   (c) triangle

3 (a) 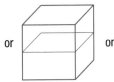   (b)   (c)

4

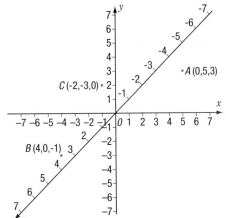

5 6 boxes fit along the length of the packing box.

15 boxes fit along the height of the packing box.

20 boxes fit along the width of the packing box.

$6 \times 15 \times 20 = 1800$

1800 biscuit boxes will fit into the packing box.

6 (a) The volume of a prism = area of cross-section × length

The cross-section of this prism is the right-angled triangle.

Area of a triangle = $\frac{1}{2}$ base × height

= 0.5 × 4 × 3

= 6 cm^2

Volume = 6 × 8 = 48 cm^3

(b) Volume of a prism = area of cross-section × length

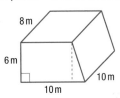

The cross-section of this prism is made up of the rectangle 6 × 8 m and the triangle formed.

Area of rectangle = 6 m × 8 m = 48 m^2

Area of triangle = $\frac{1}{2}$ base × height

= 0.5 × 2 m × 6 m

= 6 m^2

Area of cross-section = 48 m^2 + 6 m^2 = 54 m^2

Length = 10 m

54 m^2 × 10 m = 540 m^3

The area of the prism is 540 m^3

(c) Volume of a cylinder = $\pi r^2 h$

= π × 4.5 × 4.5 × 12

= 763.4 cm^3

(d) Volume of a pyramid = $\frac{1}{3}$ × base area × height

base area = 11 m × 11 m = 121 m^2

Volume = $\frac{1}{4}$ × 121 × 16 = 645.3 m^3

(e) Volume of a cone = $\frac{1}{3}\pi r^2 h$

= $\frac{1}{3}$ × π × 9 × 19

= 179.1 cm^3

(f) Volume of a sphere = $\frac{4}{3}\pi r^3$

= $\frac{4}{3}$ × π × (8)^3

= 2144.9 cm^2

7 (a) 3.7 cm^3 (b) 880 mm^3 (c) 1 800 000 cm^3

(d) 5.2 m^3

8 (a) 8.7 cm × 8.7 cm × 6 = 454.14 cm^2

(b) It has 2 sides with area 18.5 cm × 12.5 cm

= 231.25 cm^2

It has 2 sides with area 12.5 cm × 10 cm = 125 cm^2

It has 2 sides with area 18.5 × 10 cm = 185 cm^2

2(231.25 cm^2 + 125 cm^2 + 185 cm^2) = 1082.5 cm^2

9 Surface area of a sphere = $4\pi r^2$

= 4 × π × 14 × 14

= 2463 mm^2

10 Surface area of a cylinder = $2\pi rh + 2\pi r^2$

565.5 = (2 × 5 × π × h) + (2 × π × 5 × 5)

565.5 = (10 × π × h) + (50π)

(565.5 − 50π) ÷ 50π = h

h = 13 cm

24 Probability (page 64)

1 The events are not mutually exclusive, so it's wrong to add their probabilities.

2 $\frac{1}{8}$

25 Indices, standard form and surds (page 66)

1 (a) $\frac{1}{8}$ (b) 5 (c) $\frac{5}{6}$

2 (a) 1.23×10^5 (b) 4.7×10^{-6}

   (c) 5.6×10^7 (d) 2.4×10^{-7}

3 $9\sqrt{2}$

26 Constructions, loci and congruence (page 70)

1 $30° = \frac{1}{2} 60°$ $135° = 90° + \frac{1}{2} 90°$ or $180° - \frac{1}{2} 90°$

2 Right-angled; converse of Pythagoras' theorem. 9, 12, 15 is a Pythagorean triple.

3 Construct angles of 45° at each end of diagonal.

4 Sketch

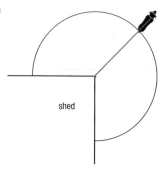

shed

5 (a) no   (b) yes, 2 angles and 1 side

6 In triangles *ABP* and *ACQ*

  1) $BP = QC$ (given)

  2) $AB = AC$ (sides of isosceles triangle)

  3) angle *ABP* = angle *ACQ*

    (base angles of isosceles triangle)

  So triangles *ABP* and *ACQ* are congruent (SAS)

  So $AP = AQ$ (matching sides)

  i.e. triangle *APQ* is isosceles

27 Further factorising, simplifying, completing the square and algebraic proof (page 72)

1 (a) $(3x + 1)(x + 5)$ (b) $(2x - 3)(x + 7)$

  (c) $(2x - 1)(7x - 3)$

2 (a) $\frac{19}{6x}$ (b) $\frac{5}{(2x-3)(3x-2)}$

3 (a) $(x + 5)^2 - 8$ (b) $2(x - 3)^2 - 14$

  (c) -18 $x = -5$

4 The factor $(b - a)$ in line 4 is 0 and so should not be cancelled.

5 $n + (n + 1) + (n + 2) + (n + 3) + (n + 4) = 5n + 10$

  $= 5(n + 2)$

6 If n^2 is a square number the next square number is $(n + 1)^2 = n^2 + 2n + 1$ and $2n + 1$ is the $(n+1)$th odd number

28 Circle geometry (page 75)

1 (a) $a = 70°$ (angles at circumference)

    $b = 27°$ (angle sum of triangle, angles at circumference)

  (b) $r = 102°$ (opposite angle of cyclic quadrilateral)

    $s = 39°$ (base angle of isosceles triangle)

  (c) $x = 56°$ (equal tangents, isosceles triangle, angle sum of triangle)

  (d) $d = 32°$ (angle in semicircle, angle sum of triangle)

    $e = 58°$ (angle in alternate segment)

    $f = 32°$ (angles on a straight line)

2 9.17 cm

3 Angles at centre are exterior angles of isosceles triangles and so $a = 2x$ and $b = 2y$

4 (a) 90° (angle in a semicircle)

  (b) $e = 90 - b$ (radius perpendicular to tangent)

    $c = 90 - b$ (angle sum of triangle)

    $d = c = 90 - b$ (angles at circumference)

29 Quadratic equations (page 78)

1 (a) $x = \pm 7$ (b) $x = 0$ or $x = -8$

  (c) $x = 2$ or $x = 5$ (d) $x = 1$ or $x = -6$

2 (a) $x = 0.851$ or $x = -2.35$ (b) $x = 3.43$ or $x = 1.16$

30 Simultaneous linear and quadratic equations and loci (page 80)

1 (a) $x = 2$ and $y = 8$ or $x = -2.5$ and $y = 12.5$

  (b) $x = 4$ and $y = 0$ or $x = 2.4$ and $y = -3.2$

2 $y = -x$

31 Similar shapes (page 83)

1 (a) True   (b) False   (c) True

2 Longest side = 20 cm, third side = 17.5 cm

3 Angles in all 3 are $x°$, 90° and $(90 - x)°$

4 (a) $1 : 10$ (b) 40 m   (c) $3\,m^3$

5 (a) $1 : 50$ (b) 28 cm   (c) $45\,m^2$ (d) $1200\,cm^3$

32 Direct and inverse proportion (page 85)

1 32

2 $\frac{1}{4}$

33 Vectors (page 87)

1

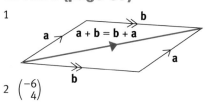

2 $\begin{pmatrix} -6 \\ 4 \end{pmatrix}$

34 Transformations of functions (page 89)

1 (a) $2x^3 + 1$ (b) $8x^3 + 2$

2 Translation given by the vector $\begin{pmatrix} 3 \\ -5 \end{pmatrix}$

3 $y = \frac{x^2}{9}$